Contents

Foreword

Physical activity is good for you, whatever your age. There is now extremely strong research evidence for the beneficial effect of physical activity on many aspects of health, notably in reducing the risk of cardiovascular disease. And in later life the benefits of an active lifestyle become even more profound, playing a vital role in helping people to keep mobile and maintain independent lives as the years progress.

Yet while people place a high value on their health, and tend to recognise the contribution that an active lifestyle can make, only a minority of people aged over 50 actually take part in sufficient physical activity to benefit their health. Physical activity participation in general appears to be declining, so while people tend to *want* to live active lives, many factors intervene, making it difficult for them to be as physically active as they would like.

In order to begin to understand these complex issues, the Health Education Authority commissioned this qualitative study. We aimed to investigate what people in the 50+ age group actually thought about physical activity, what motivated them to try various activities, and most importantly, what were the important factors that discouraged them from taking part. It is hoped that such an insight into people's views will provide valuable pointers for all those involved in the challenging task of promoting health-enhancing physical activity.

Nick Cavill
HEA Physical Activity Account Manager

Summary and recommendations

The study

The aim of this qualitative research study was to explore experiences, attitudes, barriers and motivations with regard to physical activity among people over the age of 50. It is based on eight focus groups and ten in-depth interviews with respondents living independently, and three focus groups with residents of residential care homes. The study was commissioned by the Health Education Authority (HEA) and undertaken by Social & Community Planning Research (SCPR) in October 1996.

The qualitative nature of the study's findings does not allow any statistical conclusions to be drawn about perceptions or behaviours. Rather, the purpose is to explore the range of perceptions and beliefs and the various factors influencing them.

Physical activity and health: key beliefs

- There was a widespread belief that physical activity is beneficial and that it ought to be done for health reasons.

- Physical activity was thought necessary for general fitness and well-being, as well as for a range of more specific benefits, including avoiding stiffness, weight control, the effect on the heart, stress reduction and other mental benefits. The prevention of future illness, or increased chances of recovery, were also mentioned, as well as the beneficial effect of physical activity on some health problems.

- People in their fifties and sixties seemed more aware of specific health benefits. Having noted information in the media, older people stressed 'feeling better' and social benefits rather than physiological effects as being the benefits of physical activity, and they were more likely to base their views on 'common sense'.

- There was, however, a strong perception that physical activity could be dangerous, especially 'at our age'. Moderation was needed – gentler forms of exercise than when they were younger. The appropriate amount was thought to depend on individual fitness and capabilities. The idea of getting out of breath, or an increased heartbeat, alarmed many people and there was debate about whether or not exertion was wise.

- Universal prescriptions regarding beneficial levels of physical activity seemed inappropriate, especially to older people and to several in younger age groups. 'It's down to the individual', they said. Awareness of specific health prescriptions relating to exercise that had been promoted in the media seemed low, except among some younger respondents, or others who had been advised by health professionals and, even here, there was mixed recall of details.

- In contrast to the majority view, a minority was sceptical about the health benefits of physical activity. Some men, for example, saw health as down to chance – a 'health lottery' – and were influenced by accounts of premature death (such as people who died soon after retirement). An association that came to mind of physical activity with fashion – gyms, exercise videos, and so on – rather than with health, reinforced the view that physical activity was not for them.

Reasons for doing physical activity

- Whereas health benefits were generally thought of as reasons for *doing* physical activity, other benefits tended to be foremost for *wanting* to do it and were presented as key motivations. These were to feel better, to gain enjoyment and pleasure and social benefits. A few of the younger respondents also spoke of the sense of achievement or challenge that came with it.

- The wish to counter the effects of ageing was a strong underlying motivational theme. It related both to the physiological aspects of ageing and its social effects. The way that it was expressed differed in emphasis for different groups, notably by age, and at different life stages.

- While many reasons were given by respondents across the age span, people in their fifties and sixties were more likely than older people to talk of weight control and maintaining suppleness and to be motivated by the health benefits of physical activity. Some regarded physical activity as a health measure to be engaged in to safeguard their future, rather like an insurance policy for retirement. Older people gave more emphasis to social factors, mental stimulation, avoidance of isolation and loneliness, and getting out in the fresh air.

- Overall, there were several trigger points when physical activity was likely to be considered or regarded afresh. These related to, for example, having grandchildren and wanting to be fit to cope with them, entering retirement, suffering an illness, becoming a widow or widower, and, with increasing age, the strong desire to maintain mobility and independence.

- Walking, including walking the dog, housework, gardening and activities with grandchildren were the key physical activities undertaken. Dancing was also quite frequently mentioned.

Barriers to physical activity

- A wide range of barriers to physical activity emerged for this age group. For any one individual, a combination of influences generally prevailed.

- The range of barriers overall included embarrassment and lack of confidence, lack of interest, fears about overdoing it and possible dangers to health 'at our age', practical safety concerns due to the physical environment and problems encountered with facilities. Despite the fact that the majority of this age group were retired, lack of time was one of the most common reasons given for not exercising, but while in some cases this was a real barrier (for a variety of reasons), it also appeared to be a cover for other barriers, such as a lack of confidence or interest.

Several people related it to 'inertia' – the fact that effort or action was needed at a time when slowing down seemed more natural. It related, too, to the inertia accompanying loneliness, isolation or bereavement.

- Lack of confidence was a key barrier, described, for instance, in terms of it being difficult to go alone to a class or a club, having 'no one to go with', doing something new and unaccustomed and the embarrassment of perhaps needing to reveal your body or being an older person among young people.

- Thoughts about what comprised 'physical activity' were often problematic. Images of something unenjoyable were conjured up, tending to be associated by older people with the regimented approach of 'drill' and by younger respondents with the impossible dictates of fashionable exercise, such as aerobics in a gym. 'I'm not that type of person' was quite frequently the response and there was a general theme of focusing instead, 'at our age', on activities that were enjoyable.

- Fears were expressed about the possibility of their doing harm to themselves while exercising and the potential dangers of bringing on a heart attack. There was uncertainty about what were safe and beneficial levels of exercise. This led to a few respondents having a fatalistic view that the effort was perhaps not worth while.

- The factor of external practical danger was raised, such as the traffic, fumes from cars and the fear of being attacked.

- Issues relating to facilities included observations that there was a lack of sensitivity to the needs of older people, there were practical as well as social difficulties involved in mixing with younger people, facilities were generally costly and, for them, transport was a problem.

- There were similarities in the barriers mentioned across the wide age range of this study, but issues for *older respondents* were likely to relate more to their lower physical capabilities and, therefore, their lowered expectations of what physical activities they could do, to the increased likelihood of illness and health restrictions curtailing their ability to participate in activities and to the increased likelihood of their living alone than was the case for younger respondents. Complaints were made by these older people about a lack of suitable facilities for them. Respondents from residential homes mentioned the same range of barriers as did those living independently.

The promotion of physical activity

- There was widespread awareness of the promotion of health measures in general, notably concerning diet and smoking. The promotion of 'fashionable' exercise, in gyms or on videos, was seen as part of this.

- However, awareness of the promotion of the health benefits of physical activity in general, other than this fashionable exercise, was patchy. Older respondents in particular were unaware of it, except through health professionals.

- The existing promotion of this information was thought to be aimed at younger people – those outside the age group of this study – and particularly at women. There was thought to be a particular gap in the promotion of such messages to older men.

- Views were mixed as to whether or not physical activity should be promoted. While the dominant view was that it should, there was also a feeling that health prescriptions were over-promoted, to the extent that they were patronising and, occasionally, confusing.

- The difficulty of *changing* behaviour was pointed out, especially 'at our age'.

- Suggested vehicles for the promotion of information about physical activity included personal contacts, medical professionals, the media, workplaces, printed literature being available at places where older people go and classes being held in residential care homes for elderly people.

- The types of people respondents considered suitable to promote such information to older people would be both authoritative (such as doctors) and be understanding of the issues for this age group. Role models needed to be people to whom this age group could relate. Importantly, they had to be 'our age' and ordinary, not super-fit or super-slim.

- Responding to alternative wordings for how much physical activity was required, the phrases 'warm and slightly out of breath' and 'warm and breathe more heavily than usual' both sounded rather over-strenuous to some older people, being suggestive to them of the symptoms of a heart attack.

Recommendations

Based on the findings of this study and on the suggestions made by respondents, ten key recommendations for the promotion of physical activity to this age group can be put forward.

1 Media images

To redress the balance of media images
Amend the existing overemphasis on youth by showing more images of physically active older people – role models who are of this age group, 'ordinary', not super-fit or super-slim, and who possess a combination of authority and understanding of the age group.

2 Change perceptions of physical activity

To widen perceptions of what constitutes an active lifestyle
This could be done by, for example, stressing the surprising (to some) fact that everyday and moderate exercise can be beneficial to health. Attempts are needed to counter the strong associations that come to mind when thinking of physical activity – those of fashionable exercise (young people, predominantly women, in gyms or starring in exercise videos or middle-aged people), strenuous activities, such as jogging (considered dangerous 'at our age'), or else regimented activities, such as drill (the association older people made with physical activity). Suggestions that were made in this context were to promote:

- walking – importantly including walking the dog, with messages such as 'Get a dog';
- dancing;
- physical activities with grandchildren.

3 Reassure people about exertion

To reassure and clarify whether or not exertion is beneficial and safe
The thought of getting either 'slightly out of breath' or 'breathing more heavily than usual' provokes anxiety in older people, so they need to know what level of exertion is safe for them.

4 Provide information around the time of retirement

To promote health information as people approach retirement
This could be angled, for example, as an 'insurance policy', a way to help earn a healthy retirement, and be fit for grandchildren. Such promotion might take place in the workplace and via medical professionals, as well as through the media.

5 Promote activity to men

To consider promoting to men in this age group
Men noted that there was a gap in such promotions, the messages, they felt, being mainly aimed at younger people and women. Also, men's contact with medical professionals, in a preventive capacity, was thought to be less than women's – a good, persuasive source of such information. Men also seemed more vulnerable to fears of overdoing physical activity and its potential to induce a heart attack.

6 Emphasise the non-health benefits

To avoid promoting physical activity solely as beneficial to health
The benefits to health are known about and lack of physical activity can already elicit guilt and fear (or else the idea that there are health benefits is rejected, by a minority). Instead, promotions should emphasise the potential enjoyment to be gained from physical activity, the sense of well-being and/or opportunities to socialise that it creates.

7 Avoid a single authoritarian stance

To avoid coming across as patronising or condescending
There needs to be a sensitivity to the fact that blanket and authoritarian messages recommending physical activity to older people can be thought of as patronising or condescending. Recognition that there is significant variation in the physical capabilities of people at this age is required. This presents a problem regarding the use of universal prescriptions, making it necessary to suggest rather than tell.

8 Promote information via the medical profession

To channel promotion to people via the medical profession
Doctors tend to be influential authority figures whose advice is respected by this age group and their prescriptive advice is not found to be patronising if it is

tailored to the individual – it is also more likely to be acted upon. The following are suggestions for the sort of information or assistance which doctors could give to individual patients:

- personalised information regarding physical activity;
- ready opportunities for individual fitness assessment;
- personal prescriptions for exercise;
- exercise facilities or classes could be suggested at or close to health centres;
- printed literature could be made available.

9 Improve facilities

To address the need for facilities to be appropriate for the specific age group
They need to be accessible, cheap, safe, attention needs to be paid to the mix of participants in terms of their age and capabilities and personal contact is the best way to overcome reluctance to use such facilities.

10 Start young

To promote the health benefits of physical activity to young age groups
In order to avoid the next generation becoming inactive in old age, young people should be taught about the benefits of physical activity for health, perhaps in school.

1 *Introduction*

1.1 Background to the study

The role of increased physical activity in the prevention and control of chronic diseases has been well documented,[1] and for older people these health benefits are even greater.[2] Physical activity has been associated with the control and prevention of coronary heart disease (CHD), hypertension, non-insulin-dependent diabetes mellitus, osteoporosis, cancer of the colon, obesity and improved mental health.[1] Among older people, regular moderate physical activity not only helps prevent disease but its effects on preserving function are also important. Regular physical activity increases strength, endurance and flexibility, which in older people guards against falls and increases their capacity for independent living. Even frail older people with multiple disabilities may derive functional benefits from regular physical activity. In addition to its physiological effects, recreational physical activity offers important opportunities for socialisation.[2]

The *Allied Dunbar National Fitness Survey* (ADNFS) 1992[3] measured fitness and patterns of activity across England. The ADNFS showed that levels of fitness and activity significantly declined with age. The Health Education Authority (HEA) used the ADNFS data to help design a major national campaign called '*ACTIVE for LIFE*', the aim of which is to promote regular moderate-intensity physical activity to the people of England. The first year of the campaign, which was aimed at the general population, was launched in March 1996. The second year of the campaign will target specific population groups that are particularly inactive, such as older people.

It is against this background that the HEA commissioned this qualitative study, which was conducted by Social & Community Planning Research (SCPR) in October 1996.

1.2 Scope and objectives of the research

The specific objectives were to explore, among men and women over the age of 50:

- what is known about physical activity and its link with health;
- attitudes to physical activity and participation in it;
- barriers and motivators regarding physical activity;

---

[1] US Department of Health and Human Resources, Centers for Disease Control and Prevention, National Center for Chronic Prevention and Health Promotion and the President's Council on Physical Fitness and Sports (1996), *Physical Activity and Health: a report of the Surgeon General*.

[2] Young, A. & Dinan, S. (1994), Fitness for older people, *British Medical Journal*, vol. 309, pp. 331–4.

[3] Sports Council and Health Education Authority (1992), *Allied Dunbar National Fitness Survey*. Health Education Authority.

- ways of overcoming barriers, including ideas for promotion.

The age range was wide, but this reflected the HEA's forthcoming target audience. Respondents ranged in age from 50 to 91, spanning two generations, with the majority being well over retirement age. All were more or less physically able-bodied, capable of doing some kind of exercise and articulating their views in an interview situation. Most lived independently in their own homes in the community, though some residents of residential care homes were also included.

1.3 The research design and methodology

The design consisted of eight focus groups and ten in-depth interviews with people living independently, and three focus groups with residents of residential care homes. This fieldwork was divided between three areas of England.

The sample was selected to ensure diversity and sufficient numbers of key subgroups. The focus was more on the inactive than the active, though there was a range in the extent to which those included in the study participated in physical activity. Checks were made to ensure that there were sufficient numbers of men and women; participants of different ages, reflecting pre- and post-retirement age bands and older age groups; people from a variety of social backgrounds; people living in residential care homes as well as those living independently in the community; people from different parts of the country. Within these groupings, further variety emerged in the form of many other characteristics, such as household types and the incidence of different health conditions and levels of physical disability.

As a qualitative study, the aim was to describe the range of attitudes, barriers and motivations and the factors behind them. No statistical conclusions may be drawn as measurement of the extent to which different views are held is not possible in a study of this type.

Respondents living independently were recruited following brief interviews in the selected localities; the residential homes were found by interviewers in the same localities.

Interviewing proceeded around a topic guide, which was used as a broad framework to explore a range of issues. All discussions and interviews were tape recorded and transcribed verbatim for analysis. Based on both the tape recordings and the verbatim transcripts, a detailed content analysis was undertaken. Analytical charts were constructed, summarising the beliefs, attitudes, behaviours and experiences of respondents in relation to each of the issues, identifying recurrent themes or patterns of association within the data. Such charts, together with illustrative material taken verbatim from the interviews, form the basis of this report.

The overall sample of respondents and further methodological details, including copies of all the fieldwork documents, may be found in Appendices I–III.

1.4 **This report**

The report is in four parts, following each of the key objectives. First, key health beliefs in relation to physical activity are described, and this is followed by views on its further benefits and reasons for doing it, perceived barriers and, finally, suggestions that were made regarding its promotion.

The ways respondents themselves expressed their views are demonstrated throughout the report. Verbatim quotations are shown indented, in colour and in italics and are labelled with brief background detail on age, sex, and approximate level of physical activity, as determined at the recruitment interview:

- active   = moderate physical activity three to four times a week;

- inactive = moderate physical activity less than three times a week, but would like to be more active;

- rejector = moderate physical activity less than three times a week and is not bothered about becoming more active.

2 Physical activity and health: key beliefs

There was a very widespread belief among respondents that physical activity was beneficial – even if this was sometimes expressed vaguely or in a negative way – that not exercising should be avoided. This view was also held by people who did little or no physical activity themselves, who comprised a key group within this study.

> *Sitting around all the time is bad.* Woman, 59, inactive

The benefits of exercise that respondents mentioned did not relate solely to health but to life in general, including positive effects on the mind and spirit, as well as its social value. This chapter focuses on beliefs and concerns people have relating to the link between physical activity and health.

2.1 Beliefs regarding health-related benefits

The range of health benefits described

The benefits of physical activity were sometimes expressed in general terms, as a means of maintaining health or fitness in general.

> *Well it's good for you, isn't it?* Woman, 88, inactive

> *It enhances your life, fitness.* Man, 71, inactive

Alternatively, specific health benefits were mentioned. Key phrases used to describe what these benefits are were that it keeps you supple, and helps to avoid you stiffening up. This effect was repeatedly stressed. Some younger respondents were just starting to notice stiffness. For older people, maintenance of mobility was a vital concern – that it helps you 'keep going' was the way some put it. The analogy of an engine that would otherwise seize up was also used.

> *If you don't use physical exercise, you're like an engine, you'll seize up if you don't keep everything going. You feed yourself to fuel the body, if you don't exercise the body then there's no point feeding it.* Woman, 63, inactive

> *You can soon stiffen up if you don't get regular exercise and keep going.* Woman, 68, rejector

The beneficial effects of exercise on the heart were also directly mentioned, and on the circulatory system, as well as (to a far lesser extent) the digestive system, liver and kidneys.

> *Necessary for your heart and your outlook on life altogether.... The blood flow, the oxygen, is getting cracking and it's going into all the tissues.* Woman, 68, inactive

Most people accept that a reasonable amount of exercise is good for your heart, it's good for your circulation, it's good for your liver, it's good for your kidneys, for your mental state. Man, 58, inactive

Weight control, another key benefit, was generally spoken of in the sense of its effect on the heart as well as keeping the body trim. An increased susceptibility to put on weight 'at our age' was sometimes mentioned.

Otherwise the weight goes on you, that's more effort for your heart. Woman, 68, inactive

You've got to exercise otherwise you get a bit [overweight]. I do these exercises and walk to keep my weight down. Man, 72, active

Weight control was expressed differently by different groups. Younger women, in their fifties, spoke of physical activity as a preventive measure for weight gain. Middle-aged or older men sometimes spoke of it in relation to their 'beer bellies', for health reasons rather than appearance. And people around retirement age sometimes related it to wanting to keep their weight down (and keep their muscles firm) after giving up a physically active job.

It keeps my belly down because I like beer as well. Man, 73, inactive

That's why I do it – stomach exercises to keep my stomach down because I was out here when I first retired – just sitting there eating and drinking, and the next minute someone devised these exercises for me. Man, 72, a former ships rigger, rejector

Exercise's role in reducing stress was occasionally mentioned, and older people sometimes spoke in terms of it helping to ward off depression. Older people were also more likely to mention a possible effect on the brain and that it 'keeps the mind going', reflecting, in some instances, fear of dementia. (The more general mental benefits of exercise are discussed in Chapter 3.)

Good because it gets rid of your aggression. It takes the stress away for a few hours. Working man, 57, active

As a preventive measure, for staving off future illness, as well as increasing the chances of recovery from any future illness, physical activity was seen as a positive step, high on the list of such measures (see also section 2.5). Its benefit in helping to manage or get over existing illness was also described. Some people related it to a specific health condition or illness from which they suffered, either currently or in the past, such as arthritis, diabetes, heart conditions or cancer. In several of these cases, the illness had led to the respondent taking up physical activity in order to fight it (see also Chapter 3).

You're going to suffer from more complaints and illnesses in the last 20 years of your life and if anybody goes in hospital for a serious operation they're going with the best chance if fit.... So a couch potato has a lot less chance than a fit man. Man, 58, inactive

I've more or less kept fit – I've rode a bike since I were 11.... I've had two cancers: prostate and kidney.... I was fit, so got over it very quickly. Definitely in my opinion it [physical activity] helped me. Man, 73, active

> *Certainly my swimming was for my arthritis because I know it's so good*
> *for the arthritis.*   Woman, 66, inactive

Younger respondents, those in their fifties and sixties, sometimes spoke of physical activity explicitly in terms of it being insurance for the future, of future health, perhaps 'buying time' and prolonging life. These views in particular prompted participation in physical activity (see also Chapter 3).

> *I've earned time for myself and therefore what better than having*
> *something to prolong a healthy life...this is why I'm joining [gym].*
>   Woman, 63, active

> *Might prolong my life... well if I do a bit it might make me see a few more*
> *years than I would.... You don't think of that when younger.... [So] try*
> *and keep your body fit.*   Man, 50, inactive

One or two also expressed the hope that it might have a compensatory value, making up for excesses in the past or a previous lack of exercise, that they thought might have been detrimental to health.

> *It becomes more important to you that you are fit and healthy to enjoy*
> *retirement (rather than when you're 25 or 30 that doesn't matter a jot).*
> *Therefore at our age the incentive would be the thought that I've got kids*
> *or grandchildren or whatever and I want another five years or ten if I can*
> *claw that back – if I can wipe out all the bad years where I've eaten the*
> *wrong things – whether it's true or not I can convince myself that by*
> *doing the right things now....*   Working man, 58, inactive

Increased consciousness of health-related benefits of physical activity 'at our age'

Therefore, at this age, leading up to retirement, physical activity could assume a greater importance. Physical indicators of ageing, such as hints of arthritis, sluggishness, weight gain, as well as thoughts of retirement ahead, made it all the more important to be fit to enjoy retirement.

> *Probably does become more important as you get older. I think as you*
> *get older you need to do something to keep you supple.... A lot of people*
> *sit around as they get older: they seem to think that they really should be*
> *sitting down all the while and resting. I try not to do that, purely because*
> *I keep thinking, 'Oh I mustn't get like that'.*   Woman, 56, rejector

Older people also spoke of the need to try to counter the effects of ageing.

> *One always has a fear as one gets older...will become slow and lethargic...*
> *important to continue doing exercise...like a car engine.*   Man, 72, active

> *To a certain extent you've a right to slow down as you get older, but it's*
> *not good for you. You might for a few weeks after you retire, but you*
> *soon get tired of it.*   Woman, 79, active, living in a residential home

This was all the more so, a few said, given today's labour-saving devices which reduced the need for physical activity at home, compared with all the work that was done in past generations.

*We have a lot more gadgets. I don't suppose my Grandmother ever had
a Hoover in her life.*   Woman, 74, active

This was even truer for retired men than for women as women were likely to keep
active by doing housework.

*Men when they retire don't do the physical things that women do –
lifting, etc.*   Woman, 67, inactive

A woman never retires, but men do.   Man, 74, active

Greater awareness of health benefits among younger respondents

Respondents who were in their fifties and sixties (both pre- and post-retirement)
appeared to be more aware of the physical benefits of physical activity than were
older respondents. They were also more likely to mention its immediate physiological effects, such as an increased heartbeat, effect on the circulation, energy
being burnt up, the metabolic rate changing, becoming breathless, sweating and
feeling warmer.

Older people, say those in their mid-seventies or so onwards, tended to speak of
the benefits in more general terms and in relation to everyday life, such as 'feeling
better' and social benefits, rather than mention specific physiological effects. They
also emphasised its effect on the mind – the belief that physical activity might
exercise the brain, and 'keep the mind going'. The effect on the heart and
circulation was, however, also sometimes mentioned by this older age group.

2.2   Exceptions to the positive view

A minority of respondents doubted the value of physical activity. They felt this
either in general, or especially for people 'at our age'. Here are some examples of
views that fall into this category.

'The health lottery'

A small number felt that health was down to chance, that it is out of your hands,
so personal efforts to maintain fitness might not be worth the trouble. This
minority view was expressed especially by men, aged in their fifties and sixties,
influenced partly by observations of the incidence of death or of ill health at a
relatively early age, such as just after retirement or any time 'at our age' following
the exertion of a physical activity. Hearsay, media stories, personal experience of
ill health (or that of people known to them) fed these views. Was it worth the
bother, some wondered, when it could have fatal results?

It hasn't done me any good.   Man, 55, a former miner – 'You can't
                            get a more active job than mine' – now active after illness

You can meet a thin fella of 50 who dies of a heart attack.
                                            Overweight man, 58, active

*I had a couple of friends who died and they was very active men and
suddenly a stroke come on both of them and both the same as myself they
could go anywhere, run, play football…. Is it worth worrying about?*
                                            Man, 72, rejector

Is physical exercise so good for you? People with physical jobs aren't necessarily fitter than people who sit in an office.... In the Victorian era when all the people were doing physical labour, they all died young didn't they.   Man, 51, inactive

'A fashion for exercise nowadays'

A few spoke disparagingly of the fashion element, exemplified in the growth of gyms and health clubs, where the concern, as they saw it, was more with image than health. They pointed to the fickle nature of fashion. Advice on the benefits of exercise might yet be proved wrong, they felt, as it was noted, over the years, that this happened in other areas, such as dietary advice.

People exercise for the image that it gives them as opposed to the benefit. Mobile poseurs.... Fashion, e.g. jogging, became very popular, everybody had to be seen jogging...to be part of the acceptable society in which we live, whereas a couch potato was frowned upon.   Man, 53, rejector

They tried to tell you butter's no good for you and in the last 12 months I've gone back to butter because I enjoy it.... Well, there's all sorts of things in these margarines which are being proved no good for you – cancer-forming. So I said 'Blow it, if I'm going to die, I'm going to die happy'.   Man, 60, active

Jogging used to be thought good for you, but I've read articles now where they say no, once you're over 50 it's possibly dangerous if you've never done it.   Man, 51, inactive

Related and significant concerns

Even though the views expressed above – that physical activity is not worth while – came from a minority of respondents, the 'evidence' from which this view was drawn (media stories, hearsay and so on) was widely known. There was therefore a very wide perception that, despite its potential health benefits, physical activity could be dangerous 'at our age'. This concern and other related aspects of it, described below, lay beneath other beliefs described in sections 2.3 and 2.4 which follow.

Other specific concerns included:

- *'you need to be fit to do physical activity'*

  I'd like to ask a question: do you have to be reasonably fit before you participate in exercising?
  Man, 70s, inactive, living in a residential home

- *'you need to have kept up exercise throughout your younger life'*

  Because you do worry, 'Will I be all right if I do it? Unless you've always done the exercise and you've tried to keep it up all the time, it's very, very difficult to start if you've never done it.
  Woman, 81, inactive, living in a residential home

- **'you need to reduce your weight first'**

  You've got to get your weight down first prior to going on exercises.
  Overweight man, 55, inactive

- **'there are dangers when you stop exercising'**

  *I have my doubts about the value of exercise to be honest and
  I wonder sometimes why people do it – whether it's for themselves
  or for other people, say to look good. And I wonder what happens
  to them when the exercise stops....I wonder if the secret to a good life
  is fitness or contentment?*
  Man, 63, rejector, who plays a sedate game of bowls

- **'it can become an obsession'**

  (this was not so much a concern as an observation (that, on the whole,
  was thought to be more applicable to younger people), though it was
  quite frequently noted)

  *I have a friend who goes to the gym every day.... It's an obsession
  with her... I think that's wrong. It started off her going to the gym
  just for aerobics, and then she did a bit more and a bit more....
  It can overtake people.*
  Woman, 58, inactive

2.3 'Moderation is needed at our age'

This belief regarding physical activity and health – that too much exercise is
harmful, especially as people age – was perhaps the most widely held one expressed
in the study. With advancing years, physical activities, it was felt, need to be toned
down and reduced in intensity.

'You can overdo it'

It was felt that it is necessary to be more watchful for fear of overdoing things, and
this was a sentiment that was frequently stated.

As you get older you play doubles instead of singles ...

*Tone it down a bit. [Why?] Because of the arteries and the heart is perhaps
getting clogged up. It's a question of doing plenty of exercise but probably
not at the same intensity level.*
Men, active, 65 and 72

'Gentler activities are more suitable'

Certain types of activities were therefore considered more suitable 'at our age' –
gentler activities, such as walking and swimming, yoga, and golf. And certain
activities were ruled out as being dangerously strenuous, such as aerobics and
jogging.

*It has to be in moderation at our age – it's not doing fellows of 60 any
good. Therefore you've got to pick your sport – not too much exercise.
E.g. golf or cricket – leisurely.*
Man, 60, active

> *Important to the 50+ that they don't start jogging and playing tennis…because I think rather than prolong their life they'd probably shorten it.*
>
> Man, 74, active

For older people, what was appropriate was regarded rather like a sliding scale, varying according to individual physical limitations and capabilities.

> *Wouldn't be able to do [now] what we did because of our age…well, when we were 50 we were high-flyers…still dancing and everything…. In the more senior age group you've got to quieten down a little bit when you get past your sell-by date.*
>
> Woman, 88, inactive

> *Got to do your exercises to suit your body as you get older.*
>
> Man, 76, rejector

'It depends on the individual'

The extent of physical activity that was needed to be safely beneficial to health was thought to vary for different people. It depended, for example, on a person's existing state of fitness or frailty. For those in the pre-retirement age groups, it was thought to relate to lifestyle – for example, whether or not they had an active job and, therefore, might have less need for additional exercise.

> *Everybody as an individual has their own standards – recognise them and don't overdo it trying to keep up with someone 20 years younger.*
>
> Man, 53, active

> *Depends on your fitness level. I'm fairly fit for my age and physical activity wouldn't be walking, it would be running, getting a sweat on and doing something that's making the heart race a bit more – that's physical activity to me, not walking. In 15 years' time, walking might be more a physical activity to me but not at the moment.*
>
> Man, 50, inactive

Older people especially were concerned that there could be no universal prescriptions in this respect. They had lower expectations of what they could do and were especially fearful of overdoing it. There was a need to be watchful, they felt, within the limitations of their existing capabilities.

> *Well, the thing you have to consider is what is necessary for you. Because your heart isn't so young as your mind and what you'd think you'd like to do. You've got to consider on the heart side first. To me I don't do strenuous now like I did because I think to myself, 'Oh, I'd better not do that.' Because you do worry, 'Will I be all right if I do it?'*
>
> Woman, 81, inactive, living in a residential home

> *It's purely on an individual basis one assesses one's health and says 'I can do that without any discomfort, so I will continue'.*
>
> Man, 70, inactive

> *[Need to get out of breath?] Hooey, complete hooey. Everybody's different and you've got to take it at your own pace.*
>
> Man, 67, rejector

I suppose you participate to your own limitations as far as you possibly can and then withdraw. It's like a dance, you sit down, sit one out or whatever. Man, 70s, inactive, living in a residential home

2.4 Beliefs regarding type, frequency and intensity of physical activity

On the whole, beliefs regarding what would be an appropriate amount of physical activity reflected the perceived need to slow down 'at our age' and to tailor how much physical activity was undertaken to the particular individual. There was some divergence, however, regarding whether or not exertion was beneficial to health.

Frequency of physical activity

Opinions varied regarding whether or not the frequency of the physical activity was significant in relation to its effect on health. Older people, especially, were inclined to think not. 'There is no blueprint' they said, it depends on individual capabilities:

There is no blueprint...like 'you do five miles a day, you'll live longer'.... There's no table for this at all, it's in the air. One man's meat is another man's poison. Man, 73, active

But the importance of *regular* activity was stressed by some others (mainly younger people), even if they did not do this themselves. Awareness of specific prescriptions for activity came solely from younger respondents, in their fifties, and these were mainly women. Their knowledge of details varied. Beyond the somewhat vague 'on a regular basis', 'at least three times per week' or 'every day' were the guidelines mentioned, as well as 'for 15 minutes per day', '20 minutes', '50 minutes', 'an hour'...different people stated different amounts. It seemed that although those who gave these responses had heard that the frequency of physical activity was significant they had difficulty in recalling exact details about this or had each received different information. However, they did not say that they had found the information confusing.

At least three times a week you should do something. Woman, 56, inactive

They do say physical activity every day, don't they? Or 50 minutes to an hour over once or twice a week. Woman, 56, rejector

Intensity of physical activity

Opposing views were put forward about whether or not exertion was needed and to what extent. A view that this was unnecessary, or downright dangerous, contrasted with a belief in the need for briskness or vigour in the exercise undertaken.

You don't need to push yourself at all in my opinion. Woman, 56, inactive

It does matter, yes [vigorousness]. Woman, 73, rejector

> *It's got to be brisk, hasn't it, to do any good.*   Woman, 68, inactive

Breathlessness and increased heart rate: a contentious issue

Fears of getting out of breath and increased heart rate were quite widely mentioned, notably by men in their sixties and seventies, though by some other groups also. This was overdoing things in their view and could lead to a heart attack.

> *Physical activity to excess is dangerous as you advance in years...when you get the heart beating away and you're getting out of breath.*
> Man, 72, active

> *You should slow down when you get out of breath.*   Man, 65, rejector

> *You're exerting yourself then, going past the limit. You should never do any exercise that causes you to get strenuous to the point where you're gasping – then you're overstretching yourself.*   Man, 73, inactive

> *Don't believe in overdoing it... just take your time at it.... If it doesn't hurt or make you breathless, carry on. If breathless, you should stop – there's many a one had a heart attack.*   Man, 60s

> *My heart starts pumping? – that's me, I knock it off, yeah, definitely.*
> Man, 68, inactive

Yet awareness of the link between physical activity and increased heart rate was pointed out by a few other respondents, with a small number of them specifying this as the reason for its duration or intensity being important.

> *Push that heart rate up to do any good.*   Man, 52, rejector

> *Yes, they say you should do something until you feel your heart beating.*
> Woman, 63, inactive

'Build up gradually'

Awareness of recommendations to start with gentle exercises and gradually build up were mentioned a little.

> *You've got to know your own capabilities and not go past it. It's no use trying to run four miles when you know the first week you've got to start up and build it up.*   Man, 68, now active following illness

2.5 Physical activity compared with other health measures

Consideration of how physical activity ranked alongside other health measures resulted in mixed views on the order of priorities. There was agreement on the wisdom of not smoking, but diet was the key issue of debate in comparison with physical activity – and, next to that, the need to maintain a 'positive attitude'.

Smoking – one of the worst habits in relation to health

Smoking was almost universally placed top of the list of things people do that are considered detrimental to health, the single most important thing to avoid if possible. This was not a contentious issue and did not engender much debate in the discussions. Rather, it tended to be accepted as a fact. The effect of smoking on the lungs and heart, and the link with cancer, were further elaborated on by some respondents.

> *I think we all accept the fact that smoking's a killer, don't we?*
>
> Man, 73, active

Opinion diverged, however, among those who considered the benefits of physical exercise for smokers. One view was that the effects of exercise were diluted or cancelled out in this situation, while others thought that if you smoked it was even more important to be physically active, as a countermeasure.

> *If you exercise combined with drink or smoking it wouldn't help your heart and lungs at all.*   Man, 76, inactive

Mixed views on prioritising diet or physical activity

Diet was the feature most discussed in relation to physical activity. There were mixed views, notably between younger and older respondents.

People in their fifties and sixties tended to give diet and exercise equal importance, stating that attention needed to be paid to each in order to achieve a healthy lifestyle. These age groups seemed better informed than older people about the health benefits of exercise.

> *I would put healthy eating and exercise side by side.*   Woman, 63, active

One corollary of this view, however, was that if the diet wasn't right, then there might be little use in exercising.

> *Of course, we have to have a sensible healthy diet as well, to go with it [physical activity]. The two have to go together. It's no use if you're eating bacon and eggs and bacon and chips every night of the week – fatty acids and the like – and then go to the gym every day and try and burn it off, because they don't gel together.*   Man, 53, active

In contrast, older people (those in their seventies or older) tended to place diet above exercise in order of priority or would go so far as to say that with a healthy diet there was less need for exercise. Several of these people had some very specific dietary prescriptions for good health. They would extol the benefits of, say, eating a banana every day or porridge, fish, home-made soups, a 'proper breakfast' or Guinness.... These were consciously regarded as health measures and were more precise and definite than any prescriptions relating to exercise.

> *'Kitchen medicine' is the best thing... – diet.*   Man, 76, rejector

Some, though not all, of these older people who emphasised diet over physical activity were restricted in their own physical capabilities. It is perhaps not surprising, then, that for these people, diet was the key concern...

Further, for many older people living independently, attention to 'what you eat' was of prime importance because it tapped into a wider issue, that of wanting to remain independent. The ability to prepare food, to go through the rituals of shopping and cooking, were symbolic of this, on a par with 'keeping active'. To cook for yourself was therefore most important to them, with implications also of 'mental activity', as much, or more than, physical activity.

> *To cook for yourself was most important.* Woman, 82, inactive

> *Diet absolutely on top...unless your intake's correct, your mental activity will not be correct.* Man, 67, active

A 'positive attitude' as a health measure

A positive attitude in relation to keeping going was another health measure that emerged in the course of the discussions and it was given a high ranking. It was sometimes spoken of as the avoidance of stress, believed to be a cause of illnesses, or the avoidance of boredom, but it was often meant in a wider or more general sense than that. It was spoken of as an approach that was thought to be necessary to stave off 'old age' attitudes and to maintain mental as well as physical faculties. (Physical activity was said by some to help promote a 'positive attitude' – see Chapter 3.)

> *The most important thing to keep you fit is a positive attitude –*
> *state of mind.* Divorced woman, 63, inactive – 'I'm lazy'

> *Your mental activity is really important...equally important as*
> *physical exercise.* Divorced man, 72, active

Other comparisons

Other actions that people can take to improve their state of health were barely mentioned in the discussions. The dangers of excessive intake of alcohol were occasionally noted, including several jokes being made about the physical activity involved in walking to the pub or lifting a pint. The view was expressed that, as with other things detrimental to health, there was little point exercising if you drank excessively as the positive effects of exercise would be cancelled out by drinking.

> *Wouldn't make any difference if you exercise if you abuse that by going*
> *and getting drunk or smoking all through the day.* Man, 76, inactive

2.6 Sources of beliefs

Some influences on beliefs relating to physical activity and its link with health will already be apparent from what has been noted so far, such as the impact of media stories or hearsay on fatalistic beliefs (see section 2.2). Sometimes, sources of beliefs were hard to discover, but four key sources emerged, each having a different emphasis for different age groups:

- the media;

- 'common sense';

- personal experience or hearing of others' experience;
- medical or health professionals.

Other sources, occasionally mentioned, included:

- 'other people';
- the workplace;
- promotional pamphlets.

The media as an influence on beliefs regarding physical activity

There was wide awareness of the health measures that had been promoted via the media, but the impact this information had had on beliefs regarding the specific benefits of physical activity, as one health measure among many, was variable.

For people in their fifties and sixties, the younger age groups in this study, the media seemed influential in this context. Television programmes, magazine articles, features in the daily press, exercise videos and, to a lesser extent, radio talks, were quoted to indicate the prevalence of these media messages. None in particular was mentioned by name, but, in general, the extent to which they were around was noted.

Different angles were noted by men and by women. For women in this age group, media pressures were perceived to focus more on appearance and looking good and the role of both diet and exercise to help achieve this. Although related to health, the link was sometimes indirect and on occasion found to be confusing.

> *Nowadays, hardly a week goes by, you open a newspaper and see this diet, this health – the magazines, they're pumping it into you all the time and sometimes they're quite conflicting.*   Woman, 68, inactive

Men seemed more likely to recall stories perceived to illustrate the dangers of physical activity and overexertion in older age. These lay behind the fears of doing too much 'at our age'.

> *... influenced by various cases you hear in the news....Like somebody dropped dead at a certain age.*
> Widower, 70, inactive, recently started playing indoor bowls

Older people, though they may be aware of the prevalence of media messages in general, mentioned them less than other things as being an influence on their personal beliefs. Specific prescriptions for exercise did not appear to get across in this way so much to older people.

'Common sense' behind beliefs relating to physical activity

Rather than the media, intuition or common sense was described by older people as a key source of their beliefs on the benefits of exercise. These were men and women in their seventies or older. Asked where their ideas came from, they simply said 'myself' or 'your mind telling you'. They 'just knew' or found it hard to articulate.

Often behind these intuitive beliefs lay experience, such as the discovery that they felt better after exercise or physical activity.

> *Well I've tried it, I try before I buy.... I go swimming, feel fine for a couple*
> *of hours, then I go back to how I was two hours before the swim.*
> Single man, living alone, 73, who also walks long distances daily

Yet, their intuition did not necessarily tally with HEA prescriptions relating to physical activity and health. It was 'common sense' to some, for example, to stop an activity as soon as they became out of breath (see section 2.4).

For some of these older people, their common-sense beliefs stemmed from the way in which they regarded physical activity in general. If physical activity was thought to delay or stave off the slowing down associated with extreme old age and if it was interpreted as any movement, however limited, then the benefits of this were, indeed, common sense. This was behind beliefs expressed by some very elderly people, including those living in residential homes.

> *Your mind, your own mind...tells you, you have to do it. Oh yes,*
> *you know very well you ought to.... It's the fear of allowing yourself*
> *to deteriorate too fast, it's just fear.*
> Woman, 74, living in a residential home, very active

> *Well, your mind tells you it's a good idea to walk up stairs rather*
> *than to use the lift.* Man, 81, living in a residential home

Personal experience or hearing of others' experience

Some had tried physical activity and then felt bad afterwards and these experiences could have had an influence on their beliefs.

> *I don't like the feeling of doing too much – makes me feel bad for the rest*
> *of the day. I start walking up the hill, I just get so out of breath I don't*
> *enjoy it.... It makes me feel light-headed so I don't like it.... I panic a bit*
> *because I don't know if it is doing me good...therefore I don't push myself.*
> Woman, 50, inactive

Especially important was hearing accounts of other people becoming ill or dying. For example, stories of early death following retirement, though not necessarily linked to exertion of physical activity in any way, served to underline the precariousness of life at this age (especially for men). Stories of the illness or death being attributed to physical activity – generally to strenuous activities such as jogging or squash – of course also had an impact. All these fears were behind the belief in the need for moderation and concern and uncertainty about what were appropriate and safe levels, as well as behind fatalistic beliefs.

Health professionals as sources of beliefs regarding physical activity

Information from the medical profession was a further key source of beliefs regarding the health benefits of exercise. If it was proffered in connection with a specific health problem, this seemed especially influential, not only on beliefs but on behaviour, increasing the amount of physical activity engaged in. It might relate to diabetes, for example, or heart complaints or high blood pressure.

I had angina and he [the doctor] said walking's good.   Woman, 71, active

Getting a serious illness could, in itself, have a huge impact on beliefs, attitudes and behaviour in connection with physical activity (see also Chapter 3). This impact could be almost as great if the person's husband or wife became ill or a close friend or relative. One man, for example, had learned of the links between physical activity and health following his wife's heart attack and her subsequent exercise programme and was himself setting about becoming more active.

Advice about physical activity was also sometimes recalled from general visits to the doctor or hospital or clinic. This included personal advice from a health professional or seeing literature or posters there. In this study, it was the women who mentioned these sources of information.

Your doctors always ask you, don't they [about physical exercise]? There's loads of posters in the doctor's.   Woman, 55, active

Learning about the benefits of physical activity in the workplace

A small number of respondents had come across active promotion of the health benefits of physical activity in the workplace. This included talks connected with preparation for retirement, as well as the promotion of this idea to current employees, of all ages, in a sedentary job:

Sent notices round work because it's a desk job...on ways of being healthy because they're not getting much exercise.
    Woman, 52, who works part time as a secretary/clerk, inactive

Other sources of beliefs regarding physical activity and health

Other influences on beliefs were barely mentioned. Those that were included learning from talks with other people and occasionally recalling information from literature, such as pamphlets in libraries.

2.7   An overview

While there was a widespread belief that physical activity was beneficial to health, this was also an area of concern. Two key concerns dominated respondents' thoughts regarding exercise 'at our age'. First, the idea that physical activity could be dangerous, so moderation was needed, for fear of overdoing it. Second, some concern about the amount of physical activity that was both safe and beneficial, which was thought to vary between individuals – fitness and frailty (often related to age) needed to be taken into account.

These beliefs were iterated across the age span of the study, but younger respondents (those in their fifties and sixties) appeared to be more aware of the physiological benefits (for example to the heart) and more likely to know that guidelines existed as to what are the beneficial frequency and intensity of exercise than did older respondents. The younger ones sometimes regarded physical activity as a health measure in the context of looking to the future and a healthy retirement. Older people spoke, on the other hand, of the benefits in more general but immediate terms, such as it led to 'feeling better', and emphasised its effect on the mind as much as the body and its social benefits. They based their beliefs largely on common sense unless contact with the medical profession (more likely in this age group) had informed them otherwise.

Other benefits of physical activity, which respondents noted across the age range, included its role in preventing stiffness and keeping supple, the beneficial effects it has on the heart and circulatory system, weight control, stress reduction and other mental benefits. The prevention of future illness, or the increased chances of recovery from it, were also mentioned, as well as its being helpful in alleviating some current health problems. Occasionally the hope was expressed that it might have value in compensating for not choosing the healthier options earlier in life.

Doubts as to the value of physical activity were held by a minority of respondents. These were notably men, aged in their fifties and sixties, some of whom expressed fatalistic beliefs, influenced by accounts of premature death (for example, following retirement). The association of physical activity with fashion – gyms, exercise videos and so on – rather than with health reinforced the view that physical activity was not for them.

Concerns about the potential dangers of physical activity 'at our age' often served as barriers to them becoming more active. For example, there were widespread fears about getting out of breath and increasing their heart rate and debate about whether or not exertion was a good thing. If these things happened, this was often regarded as overdoing it.

This underlines the difficulty of promoting universal prescriptions to this age group, particularly to older retired people, and points to the greater effectiveness of individual advice being relayed to them by the medical profession.

Figure 2.1 summarises the key beliefs and the perceived benefits and concerns regarding the links between physical activity and health which emerged across all ages in this study. If a theme was especially mentioned by a specific age group, for example people in their fifties, this will be shown in brackets. Beliefs and perceptions are shown in order of decreasing frequency of their mention.

Figure 2.1: Key beliefs regarding physical activity and health

Key beliefs	Perceived benefits and concerns
'Physical activity is good for you'	• Or, rather, 'not to do it is bad'. • Often more a case of 'ought' than 'wanting' to. • Minority view that it is of doubtful value – fatalistic beliefs (men).
Beneficial to health	• General health/fitness • Specific physical benefits, e.g. avoiding stiffness, maintaining suppleness; beneficial effect on the heart (and circulatory/digestive systems) (50s/60s especially) • Weight control, e.g. positive effect on the heart (and other physiological benefits); keeping trim (appearance) (50s) • Mental well-being, e.g. feeling better; keeping your mind active (older); reducing stress, depression • Alleviates existing health problems, e.g. arthritis; heart conditions; diabetes; getting over cancer • Staves off future illness or increases the chances of recovery • Possibly compensates for past excesses (50s/60s) • Hence, prolongs your life (you are 'buying time', it's an 'insurance policy') (50s/60s)
Even more important at our age	• To be fit and healthy to enjoy retirement (50s/60s) • To counter the effects of ageing (all ages 50+)
***But* can be dangerous at our age**	• Can overdo it, e.g. fear of a heart attack (men especially) or falling.
Moderation is needed	• Gentler activities
Amount of physical activity depends on the individual	• Need to 'find your own pace' • Uncertainty about what the safe levels are for me • Fears about breathlessness and increased heart rate (older, but uncertainty from 50+) • Need to be fit (or reduce weight) before you can start being physically active. (50s/60s)

3 Reasons for doing physical activity: motivators and benefits

The beliefs expressed regarding the benefits of physical activity in relation to health described in Chapter 2 were often presented as reasons for respondents thinking it *ought* to be done. Other benefits that related only indirectly to health were more readily presented as reasons for *wanting* to do it. They are discussed here.

This chapter first provides a background picture of the types of activities undertaken by older people and differences in what were thought of as 'physical activities'. It then looks at the benefits of physical activity – ones additional to the health benefits described in Chapter 2 – that were likely to be stated as reasons for doing it. Finally, the chapter highlights some factors which can trigger changes in attitudes in relation to physical activity at different times of life.

3.1 Activities undertaken and thoughts on what comprises 'physical activity'

Physical activities

Four activities in particular were widespread:

- walking, including walking the dog
- housework
- gardening
- looking after grandchildren.

Looking after grandchildren was a specific activity that sometimes came to mind when respondents were thinking of physical activity and exercise.

> *Looking after grandchildren – that's what I call exercise.*
>
> Woman, 67, inactive

> *It is physical. You've got to be picking her up [granddaughter],*
> *running after her.* Woman, 62, inactive

A wide range of other physical activities were mentioned, including:

- sports, such as swimming, badminton, table tennis and bowls;
- sessions in keep-fit, Step and t'ai chi;
- membership of clubs, such as a health club, golf or rambling club;
- dancing of various kinds, including ballroom, tap and line dancing.

The range reflects the age range of the sample. Some respondents who were still in employment regarded their job as their physical activity. At the other end of the scale, older people's exercise might comprise physiotherapy, exercises done while sitting down, stretching, touching their toes or walking upstairs.

On the whole, certain sports were specifically avoided, namely jogging, football, tennis, squash, aerobics. They were either considered 'dangerous for us at our age' or inappropriate due to ability levels and limitations.

Other activities

The miscellany of other, less physical, activities included watching television (including watching sport), playing card games, going to social clubs, day centres, the pub, seeing the family, playing bingo, doing voluntary work, taking part in religious activities, cooking, reading, playing Scrabble, doing crosswords, knitting, crocheting or other 'hand work', meditation, singing, going to the theatre, for drives in the car, on trips by public transport, fishing, playing or listening to music, doing DIY and taking part in amateur dramatics.

Activity levels

Many respondents turned out to be more active than they at first supposed. Several older people, for example, claimed to do no physical activity, though later in the course of discussion it transpired that activities such as walking, sometimes long distances, played a key part in their lives and it seemed that they were, in fact, quite active. Partly, this related to ideas about what comprised 'physical activity'.

You see the thing that's come out to me in this discussion this afternoon – [is] that physical exercise isn't restricted to organised sport of some kind. I realise sitting here that I'm a very active person really because I have my various hobbies and interests which involve physical movement – if that's what you mean by exercise.... So it's not necessary really to go to an organised session of some kind. You can motivate yourself if you really want to by being active in the home. I do my own decorating, do my gardening.   Woman, 63, inactive

The labels 'active', 'inactive', 'rejector'

It is noticeable that, throughout this chapter and the rest of the report, many respondents labelled themselves 'inactive' or 'rejector' even when they did do physical activity. Either they did not count their activities as being physical activity or did not do it to the prescribed frequency or intensity (problems with definition are further referred to in Chapter 5).

Differing perceptions of what comprises 'physical activity'

The term 'physical activity' meant different things to different people. Notably, there was a difference in views across age groups.

Older people, especially those aged over 75, tended to hold quite a specific, narrow view, regarding 'physical activity' as something very disciplined, even regimented.

They recalled drill at school, 'PT', team sports and exercise when in the armed forces. Generally, too, these were group-orientated activities.

Because of this ready association with discipline and compulsory activities, physical activity tended not to be associated, by these people, with something that was done for pleasure or that was integral to everyday living. It was only on further consideration, in the course of discussion, that a wider range of associations were made and then, perhaps, they said, walking might count and gardening. However, other ordinary everyday activities, such as housework, were unlikely to be regarded as physical activity because they lacked an element of deliberation – 'you don't put yourself out to do them'.

> *Not the other things because they're everyday things, what you*
> *normally do, aren't they?...You're not putting yourself out to do*
> *that...whereas...physical exercises, you're making an effort to do*
> *that aren't you?*   Woman, 73, rejector

> *Something deliberate to improve your physique and your health...*
> *not something you do for pleasure.*   Man, 76, inactive

Younger respondents (those in their fifties and sixties) were more likely to have a broader conception of physical activity and to see less of a distinction between it and some other activities. It could include t'ai chi or yoga, for example, as well as aerobics and dancing. It could be relaxing as well as requiring exertion. It did not have to be disciplined, tutored or structured exercise.

3.2   Reasons for doing physical activity:

the perceived benefits

Generally, a combination of reasons would be given for doing physical activity. Health reasons might be underlying them, but other, more immediate, factors were likely to be foremost, such as 'feeling better', enjoyment and social reasons. Sometimes these were the sole reasons for doing a particular activity and the health benefits were not considered at all.

Underlying all benefits of physical activity mentioned was a further theme, a common thread running throughout, which was particularly pertinent to this age group. The wish to counter the effects of ageing was behind many views expressed. This related both to the physiological aspects of ageing and its social effects. The way that it was expressed differed in emphasis for different groups, notably by age, and at different life stages, for example at retirement.

Overall, in this study, the main reasons stated for doing physical activity included:

- to feel better (in body and spirit), expressed in either of the following ways:
  - generally wanting to feel better in yourself;
  - a specific aspect of feeling better was mentioned, such as wanting to feel awake, alert, relaxed, be able to sleep, exercised, agile;
- enjoyment, fun;

- social benefits.

And, generally underlying reasons:

- for health-related benefits (see Chapter 2);
- wanting to counter the effects of ageing.

Occasionally mentioned:

- a sense of adventure, challenge, achievement.

These are now described in more detail.

Feeling better

'You feel better in yourself' was one of the most common reasons to emerge when respondents were considering the benefits of physical activity and the reasons for doing it. This was meant either in a physical or a spiritual sense. It was expressed in general terms – that is, physical activity was perceived to contribute to a feeling of general well-being – or respondents focused on a specific aspect of feeling better – for example, they would mention that it left them feeling more awake, alert, toned up, exercised, agile or relaxed and able to sleep. Regardless of any supposed longer-term health benefits, the reason you did it was that it made you *feel* better, they said, even, some said, 'a different person'. Often this feeling related to a specific sport or activity that was done.

> *I find it relaxing and I find I'm sleeping a bit better.*   Man, 50, inactive

> *When you come out [of swimming] you feel a different person.*
> Woman, 52, rejector

Exercise is mentally stimulating and helps one's general outlook on life

The positive effect on the mind was also frequently mentioned, especially by people in their seventies and older, for whom keeping an active mind was of prime importance, and by people living in residential homes. Mental or spiritual stimulation was perhaps an aspect of feeling better. It was said to contribute to a feeling of well-being or a sense of a more balanced life. It helped to stave off boredom and prevent you from 'stagnating', 'going stale' or feeling sorry for yourself. Discipline was also occasionally described as an aspect of this.

> *Physical activity helps with mental activity, well you've got to concentrate.*
> Woman, 75, inactive, living in a residential home

> *The discipline of having something definite to do is very good, otherwise*
> *you sort of sit there.*   Woman, 71, active

> *You mustn't let yourself sit in a chair all day.*
> Woman, 91, inactive, living in a residential home who
> feels much better mentally as well as physically
> for walking to the shops

Some younger respondents, too, mentioned this benefit. Physical activity was also said to play a role in reducing stress.

Getting out in the fresh air is good

The pleasure of simply being outside was mentioned. Physical activity as a way of getting out of the house was emphasised by some older people. It was a means of keeping in touch with the outside world, with what was happening out and about, who was doing what. The pleasure of walking was described by some in this way, as was gardening.

To get out in the fresh air, that is what I feel comfortable in.

Woman, 73, rejector

I walk for the pleasure of walking. I like to see what's happening in the neighbourhood – I'm a nosy guy by nature. I think, 'Oh aye, he's had an extension put up'. I don't do much else.   Man, 65, inactive

Not all walking was 'brisk'. One respondent, aware of exercise prescriptions in connection with health that brisk walking was good for you, found it was less enjoyable.

Enjoyment

Many regarded fun and enjoyment as being an essential ingredient if they were to do physical activity. They needed to want to do it, rather than it being a chore or something you 'ought', or were forced, to do. The health benefits were then a bonus. The view was also expressed that 'at our age' you were more inclined to focus on doing what you wanted to do than when you were younger.

The enjoyment could come from the activity itself (so finding the right one was thought essential) or from being in a group (notably, in this study, dancing – line dancing was especially mentioned), laughing in a group, enjoyment of the activity with others and of the music, or from exercising on an individual basis.

Fun [cycling] – I love it now – realise you haven't forgotten how to.

Woman, 50, inactive

You enjoy it as well… . It's not something you're forced to do….
Not a chore if you enjoy it.   Woman, 66, inactive

Social benefits, friendship

This potential feature of physical activity was given great importance. Whether by joining a club or exercising as a group of friends or simply walking outside in the community where you could meet people and keep in touch, the social benefits were emphasised. Older people mentioned that it was a way to help counter loneliness and isolation, that even just walking to the local shops could achieve this. People in their fifties and sixties saw it as a way to meet people, either to make new friends or to participate with existing friends. Sometimes this helped to make a physical activity that was considered worthy from the health point of view tolerable or even enjoyable. This was the extra factor, the other key motivation, to do it and to keep doing it. For some it was *the* motivation, the factor that led to their enjoyment. Some younger respondents, still in work, also found the social side relaxing.

You get bored, you see. I'm like a good many of us, I'm on my own, there's a lot of us like that. But, you see, if you go out [walking] you most likely bump into somebody, have a little chat.
Woman, 81, inactive, living in a residential home

Taking exercise or joining a club could be a social thing as well. That's very important. I can't say as it makes me any fitter, but it's enjoyable [dancing]. It takes my mind off work.   Man, 50, inactive

The social value of doing physical activity with family members (especially grand-children) was also mentioned in this context.

Health benefits – countering the effects of ageing

The widespread beliefs regarding the health benefits of exercise have been discussed in Chapter 2. Here, therefore, the focus is more on the way that these translated into motivations to do physical activity, the link with behaviour rather than beliefs. Very many people thought that they *ought* to exercise and were aware of specific physiological benefits, but still did not necessarily do it. Of those who did, the factors mentioned above – feeling better, enjoyment, social benefits – were often the key reasons given for this. Health-related reasons for doing physical activity were, however, expressed as follows.

To maintain general suppleness and agility

Strength was rarely mentioned. Perhaps there was a belief that physical activity was less likely to affect strength and that suppleness and agility were more important as they affected mobility.

Better to be agile – I'm nothing like as agile as I was but I still like to feel I can pick my granddaughter up. And if you run for the bus, it's nice to think you can actually get on the bus without wheezing.
Woman, 54, rejector

To control weight

This was mentioned a little as a reason for doing physical activity by women in their fifties and by recently retired men noticing that they were gaining weight.

To cope with grandchildren

I think it helps you keep young. You can't cope with the grandchildren unless you do that.   Woman, 69, rejector

To help prevent future illness or help increase chances of recovery if presently unwell

You're going to suffer from more complaints and illnesses in the last 20 years of your life and if anybody goes into hospital for a serious operation, they're going with the best chance if fit.... So a couch potato has a lot less chance than a fit man.   Man, 58, inactive

Question of fear comes into it... that as they get older, they are going to have some serious illness... perhaps if we sit down and rest.
                                                                      Man, 70, inactive

To help to manage an existing health problem

When health could no longer be taken for granted, this rose to being a key, rather than an underlying, reason for taking up physical activity.

Certainly my swimming was for my arthritis because I know it's so good for the arthritis.   Woman, 66, inactive

To 'keep going', mentally and physically, to stave off old age and maintain independence

For some older people (those 70 and older), 'not to be a burden' was an aspect of this (see section 3.3 below).

If you don't keep active it makes you old earlier.   Woman, 73, rejector

To live longer

This was quite rarely directly expressed.

Might prolong my life...well if I do a bit it might make me see a few more years than I would.... You don't think of that when younger.... [So] try and keep your body fit.   Man, 50, inactive

Adventure, challenge, achievement

Occasionally, physical activity was spoken of by the youngest respondents in this study as a means of providing challenge and adventure.

I like adventure – like I like to climb up the mountains and things.... I like there to be a purpose for it – not just the exercise but you're getting somewhere as well. There's a bit of excitement involved in it.... Not competition. E.g., climb up a mountain in Switzerland, which I've done, or go sailing somewhere long distance. It's all exercise. Going for a cycle, there's an objective in mind. At least you're doing something – not just sitting there in the house just jumping up and down on the spot – but there's a purpose behind it.... Yes, I think it is good for you if you're using your body.... [But] mostly I do it because of the adventure.
                                                                      Man, 51, inactive

Some older people – those in their sixties and seventies – also stressed the satisfaction of achievement in doing a particular physical activity or, more broadly, in achieving fitness through it.

> *Satisfaction all in itself because I've kept fit and you know when you see someone about 55 or 60 struggling and I walk past them – that to me is through being fit.*   Man, 73, active

3.3 Taking up activities: motivators at different times of life

More immediate triggers to physical activity that had worked in practice for respondents in this study included:

- personal encouragement, say, from a spouse or friend;

- the right facilities, for example, finding a 'really good class which feels right for my age group' or a concessionary pass to the swimming pool;

- as a response to the onset of an illness or health problem and attempts to keep this at bay by means of physical activity;

- their doctor's recommendation;

- getting a dog.

> *Now I walk more than most people here because I've got a dog and I have to go out. I have an incentive, basically, a Border Collie who needs a lot of exercise.*   Man, 66, active

- as a response to physical reminders of ageing and mortality;

- as a response to becoming a widow or widower.

This list contains a mix of factors covering 'structural' or 'external' aspects (facilities, encouragement) as well as personal reasons (facilities are discussed more in Chapter 4 and promotion in Chapter 5). Personal reasons for doing physical activity, at different times of life are elaborated on below.

A changing focus on physical activity at different times of life

Reasons for doing physical activity were noted to change throughout life. Several respondents had enjoyed competitive sport when they were younger or had been active in other ways, for example in the armed forces, or through a physically active job or because they were looking after a young family. Now, 'at our age', there was a greater preoccupation with physical activity and health.

> *Reasons for doing exercise change through life, e.g. competitive sport for younger people. As you get older, it's 'I really ought to do more'.*   Man, 58, inactive

> *You don't realise the benefits when younger because it was something you'd always done…. It's only as you get older you suddenly find 'I can't touch my toes'.*   Woman, 74, active

Awareness of ageing, of physical changes to the body, made the issue of health and fitness more central for many people from their fifties on. Ways of maintaining fitness, such as doing physical activities, became more important, strengthening the 'ought' factor regarding exercise.

> *This stage, mid-fifties, you think 'we're going to have to start buying time – we're going to have to do something' – there might just be a chance that exercise now will give me two or three good years later on and it's worth going for it.* Man, 53, rejector

> *It's like taking out an insurance policy.* Man, 58, inactive

Among those who had been fairly active in younger life, the reasons for doing exercise sometimes changed, with an increased slant towards health, rather than other reasons, as they got older. Among people who had been less active, these changes could be sufficient to trigger action. This age group, the fifties and sixties, also appeared to have a greater awareness of the physiological benefits of physical activity (see Chapter 2).

In older age, the concern was similar but was often more specifically geared towards maintaining mobility and independence, as well as avoiding isolation and loneliness.

It was therefore apparent that there were several life stage factors, both physical and social, pertinent to this age group that could trigger people into involvement in physical activity and which lay behind their attitudes and beliefs. These, combined with the right encouragement and facilities, were behind their motivations. The factors are listed below in approximate life stage order (a key factor for many middle-aged people was retirement, while for older people the main concern was to retain independence):

- children leaving home;
- wanting to play with grandchildren;
- physiological signs of ageing appearing – menopause and other changes related to ageing;
- retirement (either their own or that of their spouse);
- the onset of ailments or an illness, as well as possible side-effects, such as weight gain;
- becoming a widow or widower;
- wanting to maintain mobility and independence.

Let us now look at each of these to see how they can affect beliefs and attitudes about, or trigger people into, taking up physical activity.

Children leaving

For the majority in this age group, children had long grown up and left home. Some pointed to the fact, though, that when they were younger, they had been active because of their children and that now, with no children at home, there was more need to take exercise. The only exception was the following factor.

Wanting to play with grandchildren

Grandchildren were both a reason for keeping fit and a means of so doing. Physical activities with grandchildren were repeatedly mentioned as keeping you fit.

> *Grandfathering – like us, we do things for our children and grandchildren – you go and decorate for them or what have you. Maybe that's a form of exercise that we do more than the people who are younger than us and haven't got the time.*
> Man, 65, inactive

Physiological signs of ageing appearing

Many physical signs were described that increased respondents' consciousness of ageing and suggested that action may be needed to maintain fitness and counter these effects. Mentioned especially by people in their fifties and sixties, these included menopausal symptoms (including women's fears about osteoporosis), increased breathlessness, reduced suppleness, stiffness, the first symptoms of arthritis, weight gain and a general feeling of slowing down.

> *As you get older, suddenly you get breathless – it makes people think they better start regular exercise.... Concern as I get older – am I going to have to get more into exercise? It's a health worry, a concern about your general fitness. Or the wife points to your belly.*
> Man, 58, inactive, in a sedentary job

> *I'm very aware of osteoporosis – it's a real worry.*   Woman, 57, inactive

Retirement

Approaching retirement (or retirement of their spouse) – with thoughts, perhaps, of the need to prepare for it as well as the period after retirement because of a drop in activity levels – was a key stage when perception of the need for physical activity was heightened. This was fuelled (for men especially) by real concern over stories of early death at this time. Some expressed a belief that retirement could be a period of rapid physical deterioration unless preventive action was taken.

> *As an HG driver, I was working and I didn't need exercise because my bloody job was up and down...loading and unloading...I was working, my muscles were hard. Since I retired I can feel me muscles go softer.*
> Man, 71, inactive, whose activity now is playing with his grandsons, walking 'according to how the dog feels'

> *You come across so many people, they live for the job and they retire and they just go to cabbages.... The worst time is when you first retire. Oh it is dreadful. You're at home and you're in the way of the wife and you think where shall I go?... So you make yourself active, or sit there and become a cabbage... and I think it's so easy to do the wrong one.*   Man, 74, rejector

The onset of ailments or an illness

This was a powerful trigger – using physical activity to keep symptoms at bay, slow down the disease or to aid recovery. It also brought contact with the medical profession and accompanying information about the benefits of exercise, and encouragement to do it.

Visit to the bone clinic where I was told to walk briskly, not to dawdle.
Woman, 55, inactive, who therefore walks the dog quicker now

I'm diabetic. The clinic tells you you must do a certain amount of exercise – e.g., if you can't go far, well, walk up and down the stairs to exercise, and there's various forms they suggest like gardening is one of the best exercises, especially digging.... I've got to keep my sugar down and the way to keep it down is exercise which is walking. If I go for a good walk, I know it'll bring it down.
Man, 74, inactive

I was told after my triple bypass three years ago – so they tell me to keep active. I'm great now since. I do stretching, moving the arms, touch toes, and stomach muscles – got to keep my tummy down which I was taught how to do.
Man, 74, rejector

Becoming a widow or widower

Although this could represent a barrier to physical activity for some (for example, no longer having your partner to do things with, such as dancing or walking – see Chapter 4), it was also sometimes a factor in becoming more active. Some people had taken up new activities, including physical activity, at this time, as well as taking on physical household chores that used to be done by their spouse.

Definitely [more active] because I didn't want to rely on my children.
Woman, 82, inactive

I've got to go out since I lost my husband, got to get out.
Woman, 79, active

Wanting to maintain mobility and independence

In older age, the strong wish to maintain independence, to avoid becoming a burden to children, prompted action, as well as the wish to avoid becoming housebound or to go into a home.

*Because I don't want my children to have the burden of keeping me....
If you keep the mind active, even if your body won't work, you can keep your independence in the way that matters, the way you know and understand.*
Woman, 74, rejector

You don't have to depend on anyone to come and do anything for you.
Woman, 74, active

Whatever happens, I don't want to go into a nursing home, I'd rather die.
Woman, 86, active

A further trigger related to this was the fear that there has been a reduction in services for elderly people.

*...important because services offered for the elderly as they become
disabled are being cut down.*   Woman, 74, rejector

On the news last night, at the age of 75, hospitals don't want you.
                                                                 Man, 72, rejector

3.4 An overview

Whereas the health benefits of exercise were generally thought of as reasons that
made physical activity something that *ought* to be done, other benefits tended to
be more readily described as reasons for wanting to do it, and these were presented
as the key motivations. Foremost among these were wanting to feel better, for
enjoyment and pleasure and for the social benefits they got out of it. A few of the
younger respondents also spoke of a sense of achievement or challenge they got
from physical activity.

In addition, health-related motivations were expressed in terms of wanting to
maintain suppleness and agility, control weight, enhance physical and mental
capabilities, prevent or increase the chances of recovery from an illness, help
manage existing health problems (such as heart problems) and generally keep 'old
age' at bay.

The wish to counter the effects of ageing was a strong motivational theme
underlying many of these views expressed. It related both to the physiological
aspects of ageing and its social effects. The way that it was expressed differed in
emphasis for different groups, notably by age, and at different life stages, for
example at the point of retirement.

Overall, there were many trigger points (at different times throughout the age span
of the respondents), when physical activity was likely to be considered or regarded
differently. These related, for example, to children leaving home, wanting to play
with grandchildren, the physiological signs of ageing appearing (including the
menopause), retirement (either their own or that of their spouse), the onset of
ailments or an illness and its possible side-effects, becoming a widow or widower
and, with increasing age, the strong desire to maintain mobility and independence.

People aged in their fifties and sixties (women especially), tended to be more aware
of the physiological benefits of physical activity (see Chapter 2), were more likely
to talk of weight control and suppleness and to be more motivated by health
benefits than older people. In turn, older people put more emphasis on social
factors, the mental stimulation exercise gave them, the avoidance of isolation and
loneliness and the chance to get out in the fresh air.

Ideas about what constituted physical activity also differed with age. Older people
sometimes held quite a narrow conception of it as being something disciplined or
regimented and, therefore, would not necessarily include everyday activities in
their definition of it. Younger respondents, however, thought of it in broader terms.
Walking, including walking the dog, housework, gardening and activities with
grandchildren were the most common physical activities undertaken overall.
Dancing (especially line dancing) was also quite frequently mentioned and enjoyed.
Rarely did it seem that attention was paid to exertion in the activities undertaken.
Walking for example was rarely brisk.

Further factors affecting the take-up of physical activity related to the right facilities being available, those sensitive to older people's requirements (see Chapter 4). Also, personal encouragement played a key role in this, especially that from a friend, doctor or other health professional, rather than media publicity campaigns.

Figures 3.1 and 3.2 continue Figure 2.1. They summarise the benefits of physical activity that were additional to the health benefits (Figure 3.1) and the ways in which they were perceived to counter the effect of ageing for different groups (Figure 3.2).

Figure 3.1 Other benefits of physical activity to mind and spirit and key motivations

Benefits	Motivations
To feel better	● generally feel better in yourself ● feel better in a specific way (e.g. alert, toned up, agile, relaxed, able to sleep)
Mental stimulation	● e.g. keeps your mind active; gives you a positive outlook; helps you avoid 'stagnation' or 'staleness'
For enjoyment	● for pleasure, fun ● to be out in the fresh air, e.g. walking, gardening
For the social benefits	● activities can be done with friends or it is a way to make friends ● you get out and about
For the adventure or the challenge, the feeling of achievement gained	● Occasionally mentioned by the 50s/60s

Note: Figure 3.1 shows key themes that emerged across all ages in this study. Benefits and motivations are shown in order of decreasing frequency of their mention.

Figure 3.2: Countering the effects of ageing, the underlying themes

Countering the effects of ageing

- avoiding stiffness, keeping agile
- not allowing yourself to deteriorate too fast

50/60-year-olds emphasised

- looking ahead – wanting to be fit for retirement;
- a concern to prolong life – it's an 'insurance policy';
- wanting general health and fitness;
- wanting to be fit for grandchildren;
- wanting to control their weight;
- wanting to alleviate stress;
- liking a sense of achievement, a challenge (low mention);
- physiological benefits;
- the media as having an influence on their beliefs.

Older respondents emphasised

- wanting to maintain mobility, keep active;
- wanting to maintain independence to avoid being a burden to their children and because of a fear of becoming housebound;
- wanting to avoid isolation or loneliness;
- the benefit of mental stimulation, keeping the mind active;
- that it was good to get out into the fresh air;
- wanting to be fit for grandchildren;
- enjoyment and socialising were important;
- that they had lower expectation of what they would be able to do;
- the importance of diet more than physical activity;
- 'common sense' and information from medical professionals as being the source of their beliefs.

4 Perceived barriers to physical activity

This chapter looks at why many people – though generally they knew that physical activity was beneficial – remained physically inactive.

4.1 The range of barriers

'Barriers' to physical activity, for any individual, were likely to comprise a combination of influences. A mix of the internal (attitudes, beliefs, feelings, expectations) and the external (facilities, environment and physical limitations) had an impact on respondents' behaviour. These, in turn, may relate to their particular history of exercise and whether or not they will continue to be physically active.

Some barriers will already be apparent. Concerns and uncertainties about what constitutes safe levels of physical activity, for example, have been described in Chapter 2. There are also echoes in this chapter of Chapter 3, as it is apparent that some of the factors discussed there that serve as motivators can also be construed as barriers to physical activity.

Overall, a wide range of factors were presented as barriers. It is difficult to arrange these factors in an order of emphasis because of the variety across the study between individuals, and, to an extent, by age group and by sex. 'Inertia' is placed at the top of the list opposite because it was a key factor, underlying many others. Despite the fact that the majority of respondents were retired, lack of time was one of the most frequently quoted barriers, though this belied the variety behind it. Factors that are to do with attitude follow this first factor, then external difficulties and issues relating to the provision of facilities.

Although there are some differences in barriers for the various age bands, it is interesting to note that the similarities were more striking than the differences. Extent of frailty, illness or disability is perhaps a better indicator of difference in this respect than age, affecting as it does ideas of what can constitute appropriate 'physical activity' meaning that for some elderly people, sharing facilities, such as swimming pools, with energetic young people is not ideal, to say the least. Life stages, such as losing a spouse, retirement, the arrival of grandchildren and so on, were also relevant, for some, when considering barriers, as they were in relation to motivations for undertaking physical activity. Attention to all these points is highlighted in relation to the particular barriers as they become relevant.

The barriers to physical activity mentioned by respondents were as follows:

- inertia:
  - the effort of doing something:
    - in general;
    - related to loneliness, isolation, bereavement;
  - 'slowing down':
    - began noticing their age, and their attitudes to exercise were changing (younger respondents);
    - physical constraints (older respondents);

- no time:
  - in general;
  - due to work (pre-retirement);
  - due to the activities of retirement or changed perceptions of time;
  - duties and attitudes of some women (and widowed men);
  - as a grandparent;
  - as a carer;
  - effects of illness, such as a treatment programme;

- lack of interest:
  - 'not that type of person';
  - narrow or negative conception of what physical activity is;
  - tried it and disliked it;
  - reluctance 'at our age' to do activities that are not enjoyed;
  - since widowed, a lack of interest in what had been joint activities;

- embarrassment, shyness, lack of confidence about:
  - revealing your body;
  - being older among young people;
  - doing something new and unaccustomed;
  - supposedly lacking skills;
  - being alone, having no one to go with;

- possible dangers to health, a fear of overdoing it:
  - in general 'at our age';
  - because of a specific concern, such as a heart attack;
  - because of an existing health problem;
  - because of the possibility of 'addiction';

- external dangers or difficulties:
  - a hostile physical environment (traffic, climate, fumes, fears of attack);
  - a hostile social environment;

- problems with facilities:
  - a lack of facilities;
  - inappropriate facilities;
  - cost;
  - transport problems.

Inertia

The effort of doing something

This barrier to the take-up of physical activity related to the *effort* it required, that it was simply easier not to do something, than to do it. Some respondents ascribed this to general laziness or else cited the effort of, say, getting the bicycle out of the garage or of going out to the swimming pool or to any other place for physical activity.

> *Up here [points to head] I'm 18. When I see that chap with the grey hair and double chin [in the mirror], that isn't me, that's somebody else.... But...a bit of exercise you think, 'Oh, I just can't be bothered'.*
>
> Man, 58, active

> *Might not have the initiative to get up and go.... Lady next door just sits watching the box.*
>
> Woman, 55, inactive

This barrier does not include the effort needed to overcome physical problems or illnesses of older age, though of course these can present a very real barrier, as we shall see below. Rather, it relates to the mental or emotional frame of mind, and was apparent among the respondents to varying degrees. At one end of the scale, it could be a case of simply 'getting in a rut' or, as some put it, lacking the discipline. At the other end of the scale, it was an aspect of loneliness or isolation, an inertia brought on by being alone, which could be acute at specific times, such as bereavement.

> *A lot of people who have been widowed, if it hadn't been for someone like me who's got plenty of get up and go, they wouldn't have done anything [re physical activity].*
>
> Woman, 66, inactive, who recently joined an exercise club

> *It's so easy to sit still and it takes something to get up and say, 'Right, I'll do it, and then I'll feel better'.*
>
> Woman, 73, inactive, living in a residential home

Inertia due to 'slowing down'

A slowing down, attributed to ageing, was mentioned by some respondents, both younger and older. Some in their fifties, for example, perhaps starting to notice signs of ageing or nearing retirement age, were of the view that they should begin to take things easy. They wanted a rest and saw this as 'natural'. It was a factor behind their reluctance to do physical activity. To older people, especially those living in residential homes, the slowing down tended to be more pronounced. In many cases, it presented a real physical barrier rather than simply a belief that leads to inertia.

> *I find an awful lot of people our age, they think about exercise a lot, but very few do anything about it. As they get older, they slow down and they can't be bothered – it's hit me like that, I've slowed right down.*
>
> Man, 55, active

Some people, I think, feel they've reached a point in their life where
they've worked all their lives and they just want a rest, I suppose...and
I think we all like to sit down. Woman, 50, inactive

You get slower, that's the point. You just get slower.
Woman, 79, active, living in a residential home

No time

'No time' was often stated as a reason for not doing physical activity and there
were many and varied explanations for this. Invited to elaborate further, some
people found it hard to explain why they had no time or where their time went.
'No time' was sometimes an easier way of covering for a lack of interest or lack of
confidence or inertia or other barriers. There were many aspects.

Time can be a great excuse for not doing. Woman, 68, inactive

A few of the younger respondents, still in employment, cited their long working
hours or patterns of working and the related fatigue during non-working hours as
the reasons for their finding exercise difficult to fit in. Otherwise, if not for
themselves, they supposed this to be a reason behind other working people's lack
of physical exercise.

My work is such lately that it prevents me.
Man, 51, active, who did karate when he was
in another job, on shift work

Others, now retired, pointed to the many activities of their retirement, whether
running the house and garden or whatever – activities that were not thought of as
'physical activity'. 'The day just goes' and 'however did I find the time to work?'
were phrases that were very frequently said or 'time seems to pass quicker',
sometimes without their realising how.

I wouldn't have the time by the time I've done my housework and cooked
a dinner and taken the dog out and gone shopping, gone to my friend's....
Hard time to fit anything else in. Woman, 73, rejector – still
wouldn't do it if had time as this lack
of time relates to lack of interest

The day just goes. Well, I do decorating, I walk the dog, I've got my own
garden and allotment to look after. I keep busy. Man, 60, active

Some recently retired people also now started the day later – there seemed fewer
hours available in that sense, too.

Well you've got a different outlook on life...when I was going to work I
was quite happy to get up at 6 o'clock, but this year not before 7.30.
Man, 57, active

The only reason you lapse [in doing exercise] is if you get up too late...
Man, 53, inactive, who gets up too late to do his exercises now

Time taken up by 'being a grandparent' was a specific aspect mentioned (though in other cases this was a trigger or motivator to undertake more physical activity, having a significant someone to exercise with or for – see Chapter 3).

> *I think when you become a grandfather you often wonder how you had*
> *the time to go to work.*   Man, 74, rejector

Women sometimes described their lack of time as being due to their roles and responsibilities in the home or family. Whether this was down to doing housework or because they were entrenched in a tradition of putting other people's needs first, 'as a female' they felt they had less time for other things, such as physical activity.

> *I think as a female you think, 'Oh, that'll need doing so I won't go'*
> *[and do physical activity]. I'd love to do more walking, but I think, 'Oh,*
> *I'll clean a cupboard out'.... I get this terrible guilt.*   Woman, 55, inactive

> *I think it's time as well. I do so many other things and I should say no*
> *to some of them and perhaps give more time to doing some exercise....*
> *It's just getting your life organised. Really I think you need to be more*
> *selfish sometimes. I think you need to say, 'I need this time'.... But*
> *you don't. [As a woman] I certainly would put somebody else first.*
>   Woman, 57, inactive

Interestingly, some men also attributed a lack of time to the extra burden of household chores, once they were widowed and managing on their own.

> *... she [was the one who] looked after the house and I looked after the*
> *garden.... When you get older, it seems like the law of diminishing returns*
> *comes in.... because they [people] are doing things they've never done*
> *before – all the things you got somebody else to do, I do myself.*
>   Widower, 76, rejector

For those people who had a health problem, such as some in residential homes as well as some others living independently, the effects of their illness could take up their time.

> *... with people like ourselves it probably takes something like a couple of*
> *hours to get motivated enough during the course of the morning. It takes*
> *time... you're very slow.... I've got something like an hour's treatment*
> *programme to go through.*   Man, 70s, inactive, living in
>   a residential home, who suffers from emphysema

Lack of interest

Some people said quite plainly that they just did not enjoy physical activity, and neither did they find it pleasurable. They were not 'that type of person', they said, as if one had to be of a certain temperament to have a physically active lifestyle. Often, however, this view related to the type of thing that came into their minds when they thought of physical activity. They generally had quite a narrow conception of it, especially the older respondents (see Chapter 3). They thought of specific exercises, such as the 'up, down, bend' of 'drill', or a particular sport or activity. On consideration, however, some of these people acknowledged that they probably would enjoy other types of activities, such as dancing, for instance. There was a reluctance 'at our age' to do things were not enjoyable.

> *I don't like exercise...I find it bizarre that anybody would want to do that.*
>
> Man, 53, rejector

> *No, not [pleasurable] to me. I know it's funny, but it's just the way I'm made.... Don't think it's my temperament to do it. It's not much of an interest. I would have to make a very hard effort to do it because I don't like it. I've never been an exercise-type person...never liked anything like that.*
>
> Woman, 73, rejector

Others based their dislike on personal experience of physical activity. They had found it tiring, for example, or felt that their physical capabilities were no longer up to it.

> *I don't get high [as others do, on physical activity]. I feel quite shattered and tired and so I don't feel good.... I wish I hadn't done it sometimes. It makes me feel quite fatigued.*
>
> Woman, 54, rejector

People who were widowed and who had been accustomed to taking part in some form of physical activity, such as walking or dancing, jointly with their husband or wife sometimes stopped doing so because they found it less enjoyable to do it alone.

Embarrassment, shyness, lack of confidence

A lack of confidence about doing physical activity seemed a strong disincentive. This took various forms. For example, people were self-conscious about revealing their bodies, fearful of being shown up in front of younger people or embarrassed about trying something new, not quite knowing what to expect; or (much mentioned) daunted at the thought of entering a group of strangers. Many of these instances related specifically to age, to being older, and a self-consciousness about this. They were demonstrated in all the age groups of this study, so let us look at them a bit more closely.

Embarrassment about revealing your body

Respondents did not want to reveal themselves in a class of others, especially if they were overweight. Even doing exercises at home could be considered embarrassing in this respect.

> *I don't like to show my body off...I like to walk along and leisurely take in the things around me. I don't like being in a crowd showing my body because I'm a bit shyish. I don't like that kind of activity. I like walking, I love that, and I love to look around and talk to people.*
>
> Woman, 79, active, referring to her reasons for shunning the keep-fit sessions at her residential home

> *[Re Mr Motivator, etc.] You couldn't do it in the bedroom with your husband watching.*
>
> Woman, 63, active through gardening and walking the dog

Embarrassment about being older among young people

This was often mentioned by both men and women, but men found it especially difficult to be exercising among young women.

There's kids there, there's 20-year-old nubile women there. Man, 53, active

It's all young people – they say 'I'm going to the gym tonight'. I'm going to the gym with my pot belly.... You think 'Oh, I feel a right fool'.
Man, 58, active

Embarrassment about doing something new and unaccustomed

For example, a new form of exercise, not knowing what to expect, and perhaps being concerned about lacking the appropriate skills.

Number one, they've never done it before,... so, the thing is, it's shyness...as you grow older...some people don't lose it, especially the women, they get out of figure [shape]. Man, 73, active

You'd feel a bit embarrassed for a start. Yes, I've always been a bit that way inclined.... If I'm doing anything different, I'm a bit embarrassed.
Woman, 73, rejector

Embarrassment about being alone, having no one to go with

The difficulty of joining something new, such as a club or class of strangers, needing someone to go with, was a source of embarrassment.

It's that initial going in and meeting people you don't know which I think is hard. Woman, 71, active

This was also so for those who had been widowed as they were unaccustomed to doing an activity alone.

Oh yes, we definitely did more things when we had somebody to do them with, like go for a walk.... It's much nicer and better.
Woman, 84, inactive, living in a residential home

Even walking out alone in public places, such as the street or park, for no purpose other than exercise would be experienced as embarrassing for some. Hence, it was frequently said, you needed a dog.

I feel it's silly walking if I went walking round the park on my own. But with a dog you've got someone with you, you feel entirely different.
Woman, 73, rejector

People look at me a bit stupid [walking] if you haven't got a dog.
Woman, 55, inactive

Possible dangers to health

Fear of overdoing things – that physical activity might cause more harm than good to your health and actually be bad for you – was a real concern to some people (see Chapter 2).

> *That chap in America who said jogging was good for you: years later they found him slumped over the fence, dead, didn't they, at 55.*
>
> Man, 51, inactive

This was expressed as either a general fear, of something being potentially dangerous 'at our age',

> *I feel I do enough now regarding activities – enough I think for my body and my age.*
>
> Woman, 82, inactive

or as a specific concern. Fears of having a heart attack were the key worry, among men especially. Other fears were mentioned relating to individual health conditions – worries, for example, of putting your back out or falling over.

> *There's one thing you have to guard against…. Chest…there's an awful lot of people that are afraid to do it in case they have a heart attack [also after having had a heart attack]….*
>
> Man, 60s

> *Like me plodding along – I don't feel particularly unfit, but I could say to myself 'Right, I'll start again' and the next minute I read in the paper '15-year-old dies of heart attack playing football'. I say, 'Hello!'*
>
> Man, 55, inactive and overweight

Based on these fears, some wondered whether or not physical activity was worth the effort. Yet, in some instances, the extent to which these were real barriers was questionable; sometimes it seemed that they were presented to rationalise inactivity. Other factors were more pertinent and some other people also held these views but were physically active.

> *What guarantee is there…?*
>
> Woman, 52, inactive, whose father died of a thrombosis at 52

> *I panic a bit because I don't know if it is doing me any good.*
>
> Woman, 51, inactive

They were concerned about not knowing what the appropriate limits were for them individually, how much exercise was both beneficial and safe.

> *You've got to know how far to go with it.*
>
> Man, 63, now very active after medical advice following illness

Other specific beliefs related to these fears were voiced as barriers to the take-up of physical activity (also described in Chapter 2). They related to the supposed need:

- to be fit from the outset, before starting to exercise;
- to have established a habit of exercising throughout earlier life;

- to lose weight before you begin ('exercising if overweight is dangerous').

To a far lesser extent, there was also a concern that, once started, exercise needed to be maintained, that starting and then stopping was likely to result in weight gain.

...since I've stopped going there [aerobics] I've put on two stone.

Woman, 59, rejector

Fear of 'addiction' to physical activity was also mentioned, but in a light-hearted way, as respondents felt this seemed unlikely on a personal level. Mainly, this fear was voiced by people in their fifties and acknowledged to be an excuse. They had heard of instances where this had happened. It was rarely, if at all, a real barrier, although it may have strengthened the feeling that too much exercise could be harmful.

You can become addicted to the drugs which are released through hard physical exercise.... (No, there's no danger of me getting addicted to that.)

Man, 60, inactive

Fears and restrictions relating to an existing health problem

The above fears were heightened for some respondents who had health problems or medical conditions. The symptoms of their asthma, arthritis, artificial joints or general stiffness, for example, presented a real barrier to their doing certain activities and increased their concern about overdoing it.

I'm not able to [walk fast/sprint] for medical reasons. You might say, 'Well, that's attributable to your age'...but it's not attributable to everybody at my age.

Woman, 76, inactive

...regarding dancing, with having the stiff hip I've never really gone to dances or anything like that...you can't dance very well in a shoe that's built up.

Woman, 82, inactive

Being physically unfit...asthma dampens it down. I go for a walk and then I've got to make sure I've got my puffer with me. Man, 76, rejector

This hip has restricted me...I'd make a different life for myself if I wasn't restricted to this. I'm frightened – I'm terrified for my hip and everything I do I'm very cautious.

Woman, 84, rejector

However, some of these people were physically active or had switched activities since becoming ill. In some cases, ill health or disability could serve as a trigger rather than a barrier, urging them to be active to combat their health problems (see also Chapter 3).

External dangers or difficulties

External dangers, such as traffic, unhealthy traffic fumes and, especially, fear of attack on the streets or in parks, were all mentioned as disincentives, both in relation to specific activities, such as cycling and walking, and to going out in general, to reach a venue to go dancing or whatever. These fears were spoken of especially in the urban areas in which the research was conducted. Although, they would be felt at any age, older people are especially vulnerable as they are more likely to be alone and less likely to have a car. The older age groups noted how the external environment was so much more dangerous than when they were young, when it was more conducive to walking, cycling and other outdoor physical activities.

> *Frightened now on the road with a bike...motorists...don't realise a cyclist's vulnerability.*   Man, 73, active

> *Traffic... – all you do is get fumes...the only thing you're doing by walking and that's healthy but what gets into your lungs isn't.*
>   Man, 76, rejector who has asthma

> *There's a lot of people now won't go out, especially elderly people because they're frightened of being mugged.*   Man, 74, rejector

> *[Fear] that is a great barrier...when I'm on my own, I mean I've got dogs, but I'm petrified.*   Woman, 66, inactive

The cold climate and not wanting to be out on dark evenings were also mentioned in this context.

> *At night it's too dark, it's not safe to go by yourself.*   Woman, 84, active

Other dangers, quite frequently discussed, arose for users of exercise facilities. For example, older people did not like sharing a swimming pool with vigorous, energetic, young people (see further below under 'Problems with facilities').

> *With all the young ones in there, they're dashing around and then you go there and, you know, you're a bit slow.*   Man, 76, rejector

Problems with facilities

Lack of facilities

Complaints of a lack of classes or places for the over-fifties, or of insufficient capacity in existing classes due, for example, to funding cuts, were presented as reasons for not doing (or for giving up) physical activity. 'There's nothing for our age', older people said. A lack of places to walk, such as open spaces or countryside that fulfilled the criteria of being pleasant, safe and nearby, was also mentioned.

> *Can't get in doctor's over-fifties exercise classes [full].*   Man, 55, active

> *Through council cutbacks, they packed it in – the night school [pool] – and at the other one, they changed the hours, so the convenience factor had gone. So it just tended to drop off. The convenience factor isn't there at times I can use the pools.*   Working man, 55, inactive

> *Are they going to make a leisure centre where they can come and take us?*
> Woman, 84, rejector

Inappropriate facilities

Strong feelings were expressed about this. Many existing facilities were felt to be unsuitable for 'our age'. Either they were too crowded, and therefore unsafe, and/or they had too many young people there, some of whom were felt to have hostile attitudes towards older people.

> *You don't want to go in with a group of teenagers.*   Man, 55, active

> *The pool has got to be clean and it hasn't got to be full of kids.*
> Man, 55, inactive

> *I like swimming, I like the exercise, I like the water…. But it was so busy…there's quite a few men there [out of work] but they don't consider anyone else…the arms are going, the legs…the teenagers as well when they're on holiday, they were a nuisance, jumping off the side…*
> Woman, 83, inactive, living in a residential home

> *They don't seem to give the time to the older people now like they do to the younger ones… the young ones consider you, being an older person, a bit of a hindrance.*   Woman, 81, inactive, living in a residential home

The costs of facilities

Problems of facilities charging prices that could not be easily afforded by ordinary retired people were mentioned and the need for subsidised facilities was pointed out.

> *Some people have hardly no money….*   Man, 76, rejector

> *We need subsidising.*   Man, 70s, inactive, living in a residential home

> *You like them [facilities] if you've got the money to do it with, that's the point, it's the money you need.*
> Woman, 79, active, living in a residential home

In one of the study areas, free travel passes on public transport were available for pensioners, as well as concessionary swimming passes. Both were discussed as being incentives to physical activity.

Transport problems

For older people who had now given up driving and perhaps had difficulties in getting a lift, there was the problem of actually 'getting there'. This, too, was mentioned as a barrier.

> *If people could get more lifts, we don't get enough.*   Woman, 84, rejector

> *I gave up the car [on coming into the home]…so it's getting there all the time [that's a problem].*   Woman, 84, active, living in a residential home

Access is a big one because you've got to take your test again after 75 and without a car, especially down here, you can't rely on public transport — there isn't any.   Woman, 61, inactive

4.2 Barriers at different times of life

Very many of the above barriers applied across the age range and to men and women alike, but different emphases may be noted for different groups as follows.

- *For pre-retired people* barriers were lack of time due to their job and, for some, an aversion to labels such as 'over-fifties' clubs – even though these people *were* over fifty, they did not necessarily think of themselves as 'that old' and were sometimes reluctant to go to a class consisting only of older people.

- *For men* especially, the main barrier was the fear of overdoing it and of having a heart attack as a result.

- *For women* safety concerns, if walking out and about, the time taken up by responsibilities in the home leaving little free time and, (mentioned in a small number of cases) menopausal symptoms such as tiredness and feeling less capable, were the chief barriers to physical activity.

The adjustment and initial disorientation following retirement and following the death of a spouse were described as barriers in some cases.

In older age, respondents' lower physical capabilities were more likely, to be mentioned as barriers, which, in turn, lowered their expectations of what physical activity they could do. Illnesses and health restrictions also curtailed their activities. As we have seen, this group also voiced complaints about a lack of appropriate facilities and the difficulties of sharing these with young people more than did the younger people interviewed. Respondents from residential homes mentioned the same sorts of barriers as did those older people who were living independently.

4.3 An overview

A wide range of reasons emerged overall for remaining physically inactive. Also, for any one individual, it was generally a combination of influences that prevented them from participating in exercise. Many barriers were repeatedly mentioned across the study, though there were also some differences for those of different ages and sexes.

The range of barriers included embarrassment and lack of confidence, lack of interest, fears about overdoing it and possible dangers to health 'at our age', practical concerns about safety due to the physical environment, and problems with facilities.

Despite the fact that the majority of respondents were retired, lack of time was one of the most common reasons given for not being physically active. However, while in some cases this was a real barrier (for a variety of reasons) and in others it related to changed use of time (slowing down in retirement), it was also a cover for other barriers, such as lack of interest, or lack of confidence. Some labelled it 'inertia' – the fact that effort or action was needed, at a time when slowing down was thought more natural. It related, too, to the inertia accompanying loneliness, isolation or bereavement.

Views about what 'physical activity' meant were often problematic. Images of something unenjoyable were conjured up by this phrase, it tending to be associated by older people with the regimented approach of 'drill' and by younger respondents with the impossible dictates of fashionable exercise, such as aerobics in a gym. 'I'm not that type of person', they quite frequently said, and there was a general feeling that 'at our age' they should be focusing instead on activities they enjoyed.

Lack of confidence was a key barrier, expressed as the embarrassment of doing an activity alone, having 'no one to go with' (to a class or club), being older among young people or, perhaps, needing to reveal your body or simply doing something new and unaccustomed.

Real fears were expressed about the possibility of doing harm to themselves by exercising, especially of bringing on a heart attack. There was uncertainty about what were safe and beneficial levels of exercises for them. This led to a few respondents having a fatalistic view, that the effort was perhaps not worth while.

Concerns about external practical dangers were also raised, ranging from simply not wanting to breathe in traffic fumes to a real fear of being attacked.

Issues relating to facilities included the feeling that there was an insensitivity to the needs of older people, that mixing with young people caused problems to them, as did the costs of facilities and transport.

The above barriers were described by respondents right across the study, but women (who were more likely to be alone) spoke more of safety concerns, embarrassment and also about how their time was taken up with responsibilities for others than did men. Men, noting the incidence among their sex of premature deaths, feared overdoing it and especially having a heart attack more than women. Issues for older respondents were likely to relate more to their lower physical capabilities and therefore, wondering what physical activities they could actually do, to the increased likelihood of illness and health restrictions curtailing their activities and to the increased likelihood of their living alone than was the case for younger respondents. Complaints were made by these older people about a lack of suitable facilities for them. Respondents from residential homes mentioned the same types of barriers as did those living independently.

5 Promotion of physical activity

The initial sections of this chapter look at what awareness there is of, and what the response is to, the promotion of physical activity. Then, suggestions are presented, which emerged either directly or by implication from the study, relating to promotional angles, avenues and strategies that could be tried that would be appropriate for older people. A brief postscript at the end of the chapter presents the responses of older people to the wordings by the HEA of information about how much physical activity older people need to do to benefit their health.

The term 'promotion' is used here in its broadest sense, referring not just to publicity campaigns in the media, but to any ways of encouraging the take-up of physical activity, including providing appropriate facilities.

5.1 Awareness of and views on promoting physical activity

Awareness of promotions

There was widespread awareness of the promotion of health measures in general, notably of those concerning diet and smoking. First thoughts on the promotion of exercise, however, were likely to conjure up images of 'fashionable exercise', more in the context of slimming and beauty than health. 'Ladies in leotards' came to mind and the prevalence of gyms and exercise videos. Overall, there seemed to be patchy awareness of the promotion of the health benefits of physical activity in general. Older respondents especially were unaware of this latter information, unless they had come across it in a medical context, related to a health problem, say.

Existing promotion seen as slanted towards younger people and women

In general, there was a view that existing promotions were geared towards younger people and women. Older men, especially, felt ignored. This view also applied to the facilities for exercise, which were perceived to be available more for younger people and women.

> *I see people waving their arms and legs and moving about...young ladies mostly, very few elderly.*   Man, 84, rejector

Low awareness of specific prescriptions for exercise

There was little awareness of the *ACTIVE* for LIFE campaign or of promotion of specific prescriptions for exercise though, as noted in Chapter 2, some younger respondents did recall some of the guidelines on what was the appropriate amount of exercise for them (see section 2.5). Also, as noted in Chapter 3, it was a surprise to some people to learn that all sorts of everyday activities counted as beneficial exercise and so there was no need to go to a gym.

> *That's interesting what you told me – I [only need to] walk for 20 minutes briskly 3 times a week... – I could cope with that!*   Woman, 63, inactive

Should there be promotion?

Mixed opinions

Views were mixed on the desirability of promotion. Some were in favour. They saw a need for, or personally wanted, more information, taking the view that the more people who knew about the benefits of exercise, the better. They pointed to the potential positive consequences of more older people becoming active, such as a reduced need for medicinal drugs, benefits for people in sedentary jobs and, in particular, benefits in the transition from employment to retirement. Men, especially, saw a need to promote exercise in connection with retirement. As some saw it, they had a greater need for promotion at this time than women, who were likely to continue to be physically active in retirement by doing housework and so on.

> *I think you've got to realise that these programmes are more for the ladies than for men – and especially as they're more conscious of their figures...and women tend to work harder in the house, doing the housework...like, I mean, I wouldn't dust. Good God! It would take... I mean I don't know. How often do you dust?*   Man, 68, inactive

> *Some people do need to be told because they have a sedentary job and they suddenly retire and maybe they need to be told you should do some exercise, even just gentle.*   Woman, 59, inactive

> *There'll have to be more publicity.*   Man, 70, inactive

Information on the local facilities where older people could go to do physical activities was also wanted.

> *Yes, we do need telling that these things are on.*   Woman, 59, inactive

Others felt that such health directives were already promoted too much, even to the point where they were found confusing to absorb and there was a potential for the messages to conflict with each other. People who felt this argued that, with increased consciousness nowadays of health, there was already a wide awareness that you should exercise, alongside the other 'shoulds' or 'should nots' of health promotion. Some resented it as a patronising or paternalistic stance, heightening guilt feelings in relation to something that they felt was a matter of personal choice. The money might better be spent, some thought, on facilities.

> *A little bit too much [media promotion], actually, I think, if you're trying to absorb it all.*   Woman, 74, active

How many times a day do we get 'Don't smoke', 'Eat a healthy diet', 'Cut out salt', 'Don't have sugar'. You know, you must have this exercise and that exercise. Good grief, I mean, fancy telling people like ourselves…we make lots of sacrifices you know as we get older….Well, I'm not in favour of campaigns as such, i.e. words and paper. It's action that counts [referring to subsidised facilities].

Man, 70s, inactive, living in a residential home

We all know what is good for us and what is bad for us. We know that to be overweight is bad, to smoke is bad, it's good to be slim or to control your weight, and exercise does help you to do this. But it still remains our choice whether we do it or not and I don't need an organisation to help me make my choice. I know I'm overweight, I know it's bad for me…. I've made a conscious decision not to do a great deal about it…. I don't need an organisation to tell me this – I know it. I'm not a fool. So why do we need money spent on organising something we already know?

Woman, 63, inactive

Overall, there is a need to promote health information

Despite these opposing viewpoints that were strongly voiced in some of the discussions, the dominant position was that of being in favour of promotion, in recognition of the fact that, for many people, it was easier not to exercise than to make the effort, despite knowing about its benefits and, therefore, any reminders to do it are helpful.

Difficulties in promotion

Difficulties in promoting health messages effectively were thought to be considerable, as illustrated by the view that people already knew the benefits of physical activity, yet continued to be inactive.

*See we all **know** this. I could get up tomorrow and give a lecture to an audience about keep-fit.* Man, 58, active

You can talk to some people and they'll just listen and take no notice. Woman, 84, rejector

That would be a hard job [to promote effectively]. Woman, 73, rejector

I think if people want to do it and they're interested, they'll do it. If they're not interested and don't want to do it, they won't do it, and you'll never change them. Man, 55, inactive

It's too late to promote to people of 'our age'

Some felt that it was especially difficult to promote to this age group as their lifestyle is a long-established one. Educating young people at school about it was what was felt to be needed, in non-competitive as well as competitive exercise, in the hope that physical activity might continue as a habit through life and into retirement.

*Promote through education, in school years, not that it's good to do an
hour's whatever – just general healthy things to do, whether it's just lifting
your arms up and down a couple of times or jumping on the spot.... If it's
told to you as you go through your learning life, same as we're told to read
and write, it comes second nature. You can't talk our generation into doing
it now – it's too late for our generation.* Man, 53, active

However:

Yes, I agree with trying [to promote to our age] – I'm all for it.
Woman, 84, rejector

5.2 Putting the message across: suggestions

General ideas arising from discussions with respondents

Following on from discussions about the attitudes and barriers to physical activity
and the reasons for doing it, suggestions were made by respondents as to how it
might be promoted. The suggestions point to a need to tread warily in terms of
approach, to be sensitive to the needs of these older age groups. While some of
them might apply across the age range of this study, others are more specific to a
particular group. Ten key points to emerge are discussed below.

Redress the balance of existing media promotion

Add images that older people can relate to, rather than glamorous youth (see
further under 'Role models and authority figures: putting the message across' later
in this chapter).

*Not super-fit athletes – have ordinary people, like his dad working the
garden and a spectrum from somebody cleaning windows, to weeding to
heavy digging. Not Linford Christie, ordinary people.* Man, 58, inactive

Widen perceptions of what constitutes an active lifestyle

For example, by stressing the surprising (to some) fact that everyday activities and
moderate exercise all count.

*You could show someone going absolutely potty doing some sort of
athletic thing, and then show that by doing 20 minutes walk 3 times a
week is just as good without all the sweat, blood, exhaustion and expense.*
Woman, 63, inactive

*Instead of having exercise programmes, have things like line dancing, tap
dancing, belly dancing even.... There's things other than touching your
toes ten times.* Woman, 51, inactive

[Promotion slogan:] 'Do it in a moderate way'. Man, 51, active

The following activities were repeatedly suggested as appropriate for featuring in
promotion to this age group:

- walking, including walking the dog – 'Get a dog';
- dancing, of all types (line dancing was especially suggested);
- activities with grandchildren.

Reassure people about the amount of exertion that is both necessary and safe

Fears about exertion need to be addressed as there was confusion about whether or not physical activity is safe or even necessary. Images of exhausted joggers or workouts in the gym too readily come to mind. Counter-images are needed.

Promote messages at key times of life, notably around retirement

For example, information could be given to people in the workplace during the period leading up to retirement.

Should go three months before retirement to classes on how to retire successfully.... The HEA has got to link up with companies... should be something in the system to get us all to lead a...healthier life long before retirement.   Man, 72, active

For pre-retired people, the angle should be that of likening exercise to an 'insurance policy'

It should be promoted as a way to help earn a healthy retirement, it was suggested.

Sell it like an insurance policy – instead of paying a premium in money, you pay it by doing a little bit of physical activity.
                                                   Working man, 50, inactive

It becomes more important to you that you are fit and healthy to enjoy retirement (rather than when 25 or 30 that doesn't matter a jot) therefore, at our age, the incentive would be the thought that I've got kids or grandchildren or whatever and I want another five years or ten if I can claw that back – if I can wipe out all the bad years where I've eaten the wrong things, i.e. that you can mitigate – whether it's true or not, I can convince myself that by doing the right things now....
                                                   Working man, 58, inactive

In general, emphasise the benefits of enjoyment, fun, improving their quality of life now

To do this was better than the more 'worthy' sense of physical activity being good for health or prolonging life.

Say it improves the quality of your life.... Makes you feel better in every respect – because you're not bored, sitting around.   Woman, 73, rejector

If it's put over that it's fun as opposed to that it's good for you.
                                                   Woman, 51, inactive

Something like, 'Have fun, get a life'. Not, 'You'll live longer'.
                                                   Woman, 55, inactive

I wouldn't do it to prolong my life. I'd do it to stay healthy....
To feel good, to live the life I live.   Man, 58, active

Stress the potential social benefits

Well, I think the greatest thing to get people to do all these things –
because there's an awful lot of people who are lonely – is to make it social
besides keeping fit. Make it a social occasion so that 30 people can meet in
a room...so you combine social, which is an enjoyment, with keep-fit – so
you really get two.   Man, 73, active

Something that breaks the loneliness spiral.   Man, 65, inactive

'Take your friends, make friends, meet people'.   Woman, 59, active

Address facilities issues

As we saw in Chapter 4, the feeling was that there needed to be more sessions specifically for older people (over-fifties, over-sixties and so on) that were accessible, safe and cheap and relied on personal contact as a way of encouraging people to come.

Gear it to people 'our age'

The view was that messages should be promoted without necessarily mentioning age, but that they should be sensitive to the needs of the particular age group in mind. There was some difference of opinion as to whether or not specific age groups should be mentioned.

Relate it to the people you're wanting to go to your club...and that's
the 50-ish women of Liverpool...and have a decent place to go.
                                       Woman, 58, inactive, Liverpool

Not over-fifties because that's too young. Over-seventies. Or over-eighties.
        Various residents of a residential home, 83, 84 and in their 70s

Avoid an authoritarian tone and a single rigid stance

This is especially important with older people. Partly this was a matter of attitude – it rankled to be told what to do. Messages, therefore, need to be subtle, suggesting rather than telling, and avoiding any patronising note. Partly, too, it was a matter of needing to respect variety in people's physical capabilities, that, due to the restrictions of ill health or older age, everyone was different in what they were able to do. Therefore it was doubly condescending to adopt an authoritarian approach. Rather, there was a need for sensitivity to the needs of the age group, without necessarily flaunting the promotion as being for older people. Perhaps it should provide general rather than rigid guidelines for what should be done.

You have to be very careful in encouragement because I'm liable to [say]
don't be condescending to me, don't talk down to me. What I might see
as patronising someone else might say, 'That's a good idea!'... Depends
on individuals.   Man, 76, inactive

Promote it by all means but don't force it upon [people]... Man, 60, active

There was an important exception to this: directives from doctors were acceptable and heeded (see further below).

Some specific promotional avenues that were suggested

Suggestions to promote messages about physical activity in workplaces and to educate the young on its benefits to health in schools were mentioned above, as was the greater effectiveness of personal contact in recruiting older people to particular classes or facilities. Residential care homes for elderly people were also occasionally suggested (by a few older respondents who did not live in them) as appropriate places in which to promote physical activity. Opportunities for keep-fit exercises and for dancing were provided (either currently or in the past) at the three residential homes visited in this study, but many respondents had not taken part in the sessions, for the same variety of reasons given in Chapter 4.

Suggestions for other key vehicles of promotion where messages on the benefits of physical activity might be promoted included relaying them through the medical profession and the media.

Promoting physical activity via the medical profession

Surgeries, health centres, clinics and hospitals were all suggested as places where physical activity might be promoted. A medical context was felt to add authority and reassurance to the message and these were places where many elderly people were to be found. Doctors were influential authority figures to many older people: if the doctor explained the need for exercise and appropriate ways to do it, then, they said, they would take note. A few feared being laughed at, however, if they should enquire about this from the doctor or that the doctor might not know what exercises to promote.

If the doctor said to me, 'Look, you need a bit of exercise' – I'll do it. I'll do what the doctor tells me because he's there to tell me what to do. That's about the only one I'd follow. Woman, 67, inactive

It ought to have some kind of medical smack or flavour to it because people do take notice of doctors rather than comedians [as in other promotions]. And it has to be amusing, but it has to be authoritative at the same time. Woman, 68, inactive

Specific suggestions for ways in which activity could be promoted by the medical profession included the following:

● Personal information on exercise being given by GPs to their patients, not just in relation to specific illnesses but as a general health measure.

Doctors often fail to give information on how to look after yourself.
Woman, 52, rejector

● Using the ready opportunities there were for individual assessment of fitness levels, especially after a long gap in exercise.

- Giving specific prescriptions, equivalent to written prescriptions for medicines, but relating to exercise instead or referrals to facilities offering physical activity.

Like a prescription for medicine, e.g. 'Six weeks at half an hour...'. Sending people to fitness places like on a prescription for certain ailments... I'd go because he's told me to.   Woman, 50, inactive

- Providing exercise facilities, such as classes, at local health centres or having a fitness or health club attached to the doctor's surgery, to which a doctor could refer patients.

- Well Men Clinics – to go some way towards filling the perceived gap in health promotion to men.

You hear about Well Women Clinics where the emphasis is on fitness...not treating illness.... You very rarely hear of Well Men Clinics.
                                                                          Man, 74, active

- Have printed literature on exercise or physical activity available in a medical context, for example in surgery waiting rooms, that could be picked up and taken home.

Placing printed literature at other places frequented by this age group

It was suggested that booklets, leaflets, pamphlets and wall charts could, for example, be sent as direct mail shots or be made available in places where elderly people go (such as Age Concern, post offices, libraries), though their effectiveness in such locations was questioned by some.

Promotion in the media

Overall, all types of media were suggested, but television and radio rather than printed media were thought especially suitable for older people. The success of non-smoking campaigns led some to wonder whether there could be an equivalent impact for a campaign on physical activity.

Here are some of the comments respondents made on the relative merits of the different media available.

- Television commercials

    On TV, because most people who aren't exercising and who aren't motivated are probably sitting on the couch looking at the box.
                                                                          Woman, 55, active

    Through the television – that's the thing that most people will take notice of.   Man, 74, active

- Television exercise programmes

    Also, they could do in-the-morning exercises for the elderly – 20 minutes every day.   Woman, 68, inactive

    Well, everybody can do it in their own home.
                                         Woman, 88, inactive, living in a residential home

- Through soap operas

  Build it into a soap for instance.   Man, 74, active

  ... the soaps, they often bring in things you've never even thought about. It goes into their mind more than just having an advert.
  Woman, 68, inactive

- Radio – this format was recommended by older respondents especially.

  The radio as well...that's on all day.   Man, 84, rejector

  In the news.... I listen to the news every day because I think one should.   Woman, 86, active

- Posters or hoardings in public places including ads on public transport.

- Local press including free newspapers, particularly for promoting facilities.

Role models and authority figures: putting the message across

Strong views were expressed regarding the sort of person who should promote physical activity to these age groups. Ideal in this respect would be someone possessing a combination of authority and understanding of older people; 'someone like us', of a similar age and perhaps the same sex as those at whom the promotion was aimed; and someone who appeared 'ordinary', not super-fit or super-glamorous.

These requirements contrasted sharply with existing role models known already through the media. Respondents bemoaned a lack of such figures in their age groups, people with whom they could positively identify. The only names to emerge in discussion that were thought to come anywhere near fitting the bill were those of Eileen Fowler, Dawn French, Beryl Reid and Nigel Lawson. Fitness personalities such as Mr Motivator were mentioned but were, on the whole, emphatically rejected 'for our age' as being too vigorous, glamorous and having too youthful an image (with the exception of one elderly lady in a residential home who 'started each day with Mr Motivator', having been advised to exercise after a stay in hospital).

According to respondents, in their own words, an ideal adviser or role model in this respect would be as follows.

Someone authoritative – knowledgeable about both health and physical activity

The need for 'someone qualified', such as a doctor, was often stressed, especially by older respondents, though preferably a doctor who also knew about specific physical activities.

I mean, you want people that know what they're talking about so that they're not giving people the wrong information. A doctor definitely to start with – a doctor that, besides being a doctor, is a PE specialist so that they know the right way to do these things.   Man, 73, inactive

It would have to be somebody who knows about it [physical activity].
Woman, 80, inactive, living in a residential home

Someone understanding of older people, their capabilities and problems

Reflecting worries about overdoing it 'at our age', there was a view that advisers should be aware of the barriers and problems that physical activity could present to older people.

Bring back Eileen Fowler in the mornings. I would watch her because she was gentle with it, not like these silly women who stand there and prance around. I can't stand them. They go so fast you can't keep up with them. She was really good. And you didn't know you were exercising.
Woman, 67, inactive

You'd also have to know that the person that's going to talk to you about it would understand your age, everything, and your ability. It's no good starting what these young ones are doing, Mr Whatever [Motivator], because that is not for us.
Woman, 80, inactive, living in a residential home

That's what I'm looking for, somebody that really understands what our problems are and how to get us involved. A need for more understanding.
Man, 70s, inactive, living in a residential home

Someone 'our age'

Not a young person, but preferably a middle-aged person at the very least, was wanted – who therefore, it was supposed, would 'know how we feel'.

You don't want some young fit fella about 35 or 40 saying 'Come on, get your arms up'.
Man, 71, inactive

They want to be the same age that they're talking to – then they'll know exactly how you feel about doing things...you want somebody like yourself...somebody that understands your age.
Woman, 79, active, living in a residential home

Perhaps the same sex

This was mentioned by a few older respondents.

It would have to be a woman...elderly woman. No use a young one telling you what to do, is it? Run-of-the-mill sort of woman, not an expert...because then we've got something in common.
Woman, 84, rejector

Someone ordinary

Irritation was expressed at the perpetual media portrayal of glamorous, fit, slim role models. These people seemed a world away from most ordinary people over the age of 50. There was a strong feeling that ordinary people should be used for promotion.

> *An ordinary guy, say someone round this table. But you don't want*
> *someone in a leotard promoting it.... Most people don't want to do*
> *it in full view of everyone.*   Man, 60, active

> *I just cannot tolerate it when I see these super-fit guys.... They live*
> *in a different world. It puts me off.*   Man, 60, active

5.3 Postscript: some responses to the wording of exercise guidelines

Two alternative wordings were put to respondents that described the intensity of physical activity that has been shown necessary to achieve health benefits. These phrases, drawn up by the HEA, were:

- 'warm and slightly out of breath';
- 'warm and breathe more heavily than usual'.

Both proved problematic, especially for older respondents. They were apprehensive that the phrases appeared to take no account of individual differences, such as age, level of health or capabilities. To many older people, this sounded like overdoing things, even symptomatic of a heart attack.

> *I think if you do it and you get too much out of breath, you don't*
> *know whether you're having a heart attack or not do you?*
>   Woman, 67, inactive

> *Don't think that is a good idea ['out of breath'] – it puts a strain on the*
> *heart – don't think you should be breathing more heavily.... If you can do*
> *a lot of walking without getting out of breath...get warm by all means.*
>   Man, 89, active

> *If you do **too much** exercise you will get out of breath won't you?...*
> *Walking, I'm not out of breath.... It's up to the individual – they*
> *might have some heart trouble.*   Man, 84, rejector

Younger respondents (those in their fifties and sixties) were less likely to be alarmed by these descriptions, but it is not possible, from the evidence of this study, to point to which phrasing was preferred overall.

5.4 An overview

There was widespread awareness of the promotion of health measures in general, notably those concerning diet and smoking. Promotion of 'fashionable' exercise, in gyms or on videos, was seen as part of this.

However, awareness of promotions concerning the health benefits of physical activity in general, other than fashionable exercise, was patchy. Older respondents in particular seemed unaware of it, except through health professionals.

Existing promotion was thought to be aimed at younger people, outside the age group of this study, and then particularly at women. There was thought to be a definite gap in promoting health information to older men.

Views were mixed as to whether or not messages regarding physical activity should be promoted. While the dominant view was that of being in favour of it, there was also a feeling that prescriptions relating to health were already over-promoted, to the extent of being patronising and, occasionally, confusing. The difficulty of changing people's behaviour was pointed out, especially 'at our age'.

Emphasis was put on the need to widen perceptions of what constituted healthy exercise, to clarify and reassure people about what the safe levels of activity were, and to promote its more immediate value – in terms of enjoyment and social benefits. The idea of promoting messages about exercise around the time of retirement as an 'insurance policy' was also suggested, as well as counterbalancing the dominant trend towards youth in existing media promotion. The importance of avoiding an authoritarian tone or a rigid prescriptive stance, was stressed as variety in people's physical capabilities within this age group needed to be accommodated. Finally, attention needed to be given to the appropriateness of facilities (they should be accessible, safe and cheap) for the specific age group.

Promotional avenues suggested included personal contacts, the medical profession, the media, schools, workplaces, printed literature being placed where older people go and holding classes in residential care homes for elderly people.

Role models used in promotion need to be both authoritative and understanding of the issues relevant to older people, and to be role models older people could relate to – ordinary, not super-fit or super-slim.

The phrases 'warm and slightly out of breath' and 'warm and breathe more heavily than usual', devised by the HEA to describe the intensity of physical activity beneficial to health, both sounded rather over-strenuous to some older people, suggesting symptoms of a heart attack.

Appendix I:
Sample profile

Interview type	Total	Living independently		Living in residential homes
		Focus groups[1]	In-depth interviews[2]	Focus groups[3]
Total	107	69	10	28
Men	52	35	5	12
Women	55	34	5	16
50–54	16	16	–	–
55–59	18	18	–	–
60–64	9	9	–	–
65–69	12	12	–	–
70–74	18	14	–	4
75–79	11	–	6	5
80–84	10	–	4	6
85+	12	–	–	12
Age not known	1	–	–	1
Married	57	51	5	1
Single, divorced or separated	50	10	–	27
Widowed		8	5	
Retired	72	34	10	28
Working – full time	16	16	–	–
Working – part time	13	13	–	–
Unemployed/looking after home	6	6	–	–
Leicestershire	30	16	3	11
Liverpool	40	29	4	7
Bournemouth	37	24	3	10
'Active'	24	22	2	–[4]
'Inactive'	36	31	5	–[4]
'Rejector'	19	16	3	–[4]

[1]There were eight focus groups of respondents living independently.

[2]There were ten in-depth interviews with respondents living independently.

[3]There were three focus groups of respondents living in residential homes.

[4]Respondents living in residential homes were not given structured questionnaires so it is difficult to estimate their levels of activity.

Appendix II: Details of the research methodology

1   Sample selection

Overall scope

The research was based on focus groups and in-depth interviews with people over the age of 50. Most of them were living independently in the community, in their own homes, while some of the older people were living in residential care homes for elderly people.

The study covered a wide range of people, excluding only those whose physical or mental frailty might prevent them either from undertaking some kind of exercise or from the ability to articulate their views in an interview situation.

Quotas

To ensure diversity within the sample overall, quota controls at the time of recruitment designated the mix of respondents, in broad terms. These ensured overall diversity in terms of:

● age

● sex

● the extent of physical activity to ensure a spread of 'active', 'inactive' and 'rejector' (as defined by the HEA) respondents.

No specific quotas were set for socio-economic groups as, without a battery of questions, this is hard to gauge for retired people. Rather, the selection of the localities in which the study took place was made to reflect some likely variety in social background. Information on educational qualifications and previous (or present) employment was also collected at the time of recruitment.

The decision was made not to undertake additional fieldwork, in this study, with people from minority ethnic groups. The timescale and resources available were insufficient to do justice here to these groups.

Three different institutions were selected, one per area, so that respondents from residential homes could be included. These were retirement or residential homes for the elderly (though not nursing homes):

● one local authority-run institution and two under private management;

● two institutions which offered opportunities for physical activity, such as keep-fit sessions.

Within each of the selected institutions, the residents interviewed ranged in the extent to which they were physically active.

2   Fieldwork structure

The focus groups and in-depth interviews were structured as shown below so that there was some uniformity per group with regard to the respondents' ages and sex, to encourage open discussion. The fieldwork was divided between the three geographical areas chosen – Leicestershire, Liverpool and Bournemouth.

- **Respondents living independently in the community**
  - *eight focus groups:*
    - pre-retirement
      - 50–64 years, men, rejectors, inactive;
      - 50–59 years, women, rejectors, inactive;
      - 50–64 years, men, inactive, active;
      - 50–59 years, women, inactive, active;
    - retired
      - 65–74 years, men, rejectors, inactive;
      - 60–74 years, women, rejectors, inactive;
      - 65–74 years, men, inactive, active;
      - 60–74 years, women, inactive, active.
  - *ten in-depth interviews:*
    - older people 75+
      - 5 men – 1 rejector, 2 inactive, 2 active;
      - 5 women – 1 rejector, 2 inactive, 2 active.

- **Respondents living in residential homes**
  - *three focus groups:*
    - Respondents tended to be older and more infirm than those above;
    - The age range was 70–91 and there was some range in activity levels.

3   The recruitment of respondents

Methods

Respondents living independently were recruited by means of brief recruitment interviews in the selected localities. This was done by, for example, knocking on doors in localities near the appointed discussion venue or by making contacts in the street. The recruitment interviews screened potential respondents to ensure that the specific quotas would be covered. The residential homes were found following enquiries by SCPR interviewers in these same localities.

Time and place

The three localities in which the study took place spanned some variety in terms of type of area (population density and socio-economic mix) and geographical spread within England. The areas were:

- Liverpool;
- Leicestershire (villages near Leicester);
- Bournemouth.

The interviews and group discussions took place in October 1996.

4 How the interviews and discussions were conducted

The discussions took place in a local hired room or, within the residential homes, in a lounge. Interviews took place in respondents' own homes. They were conducted by members of SCPR's Qualitative Research Unit, chosen because they were experienced in working with older people. In the residential homes, the original intention was to experiment with conducting both individual interviews and/or group discussions. Throughout the fieldwork, however, group discussions proved the more successful and so this method was adopted in all the residential homes.

All interviews and discussions were tape recorded, with the permission of the respondents, and transcribed verbatim for analysis.

Topic guide

A list of issues to be covered in the discussions and interviews was developed by the researchers in conjunction with the HEA. It drew also on issues that had been found to be pertinent in other research studies investigating attitudes to physical activity. This topic guide was used as a broad framework for exploring a wide range of issues. Although based on a common framework, the style of questioning used was responsive to the individual circumstances and experiences at the time of the interview or discussion.

5 The analysis

Based on both the tape recordings and the verbatim transcripts, a detailed content analysis of the qualitative data was undertaken. Analytical charts were constructed from these, synthesising the beliefs, attitudes, behaviours and experiences of the respondents in relation to each of the issues, identifying recurrent themes or patterns of association within the data. A set of charts was drawn up for each focus group and for each of the in-depth interviews, structured according to key issues. Such charts, together with illustrative material taken verbatim from the interviews, form the basis of this report.

6 The fieldwork documents

Copies of the recruitment and interview materials are included in Appendix III.

Appendix III: The fieldwork documents

Recruitment questionnaire

Head Office: 35 NORTHAMPTON SQUARE,
LONDON EC1V 0AX
Tel: 0171-250 1866 Fax: 0171-250 1524

SCPR
SOCIAL & COMMUNITY PLANNING RESEARCH

Field and DP Office: 100 KINGS ROAD,
BRENTWOOD, ESSEX CM14 4LX
Tel: 01277 200600 Fax: 01277 214117

P5620   Physical activity and older people   October 1996

Recruitment questionnaire

... a study for the Health Education Authority about attitudes to exercise and physical activity...

Circle numbers as appropriate:

----

1. *SEX :*   Male   1
                                    Female   2   *CHECK QUOTA*

----

2. *AGE :*   ....years   *CHECK QUOTA*

3a) Do you do any physical activity such as brisk walking, swimming, dancing, cycling,
   heavy gardening or heavy housework which **makes you breathe heavier and feel
   slightly warm**?   No, none   1 ⟶ *GO TO Q4*
                                    Yes   2

   IF YES: 3b) How often in a normal week do you do this for at least 15 minutes at a time?

   Not at all   0 ⎫
   Once a week   1 ⎬ *GO TO Q4*
   Twice a week   2 ⎭
   3-4 times a week   3 ⟶ 'ACTIVE',   GO TO Q5
   5+ times a week   5 ⟶ *CLOSE, DO NOT RECRUIT*

4. Would you say that you'd like to be more physically active than you are, or are you not particularly
   bothered to be more physically active?
   [*Check*:]   "I'd like to be more physically active than I am"   2 ⟶ 'INACTIVE'
   "I'm not bothered about being more physically active than I am"   3 ⟶ 'REJECTOR'

5. RECORD: 'ACTIVE'   1
                'INACTIVE'   2   *CHECK QUOTA*
                'REJECTOR'   3

----

6. Are you: Widowed   1
                        Single/ divorced /separated   2
                        Married / living as married   3

7a) Are you [retired or]   Retired   1
   in paid employment?   Working part time   2
                               Working full time   3
                        Unemployed, seeking work   4
                        Looking after home/family   5
   Other [*specify*:].................................   6

b) What sort of work do you do? [OR:] did you do before retirement?
   ....
   ....

8. Do you have any .   No, none   1
   educational qualifications?   Yes   2 ⟶ [*Specify highest*:]..................................

NAME: ....   Telephone: ....
ADDRESS:..
Recruited for: 1   Focus Group   *Date*: ... day, ...October
                     2   Depth interview *Time*:...........................

PLEASE RETURN QUESTIONNAIRES TO THE RESEARCHER

HAMILTON HOUSE · MABLEDON PLACE · LONDON WC1H 9TX · TEL 0171 383 3833 · FAX 0171 387 0550

October 1996

The Health Education Authority (HEA) has commissioned Social & Community
Research (SCPR) to conduct some research among older people, including some who
live in residential or retirement homes. SCPR are an established research institute,
respected in the field, who have extensive experience of conducting qualitative research.

The research will explore older people's attitudes towards physical activity and exercise.
We hope that it will play an important role in the development of HEA policies and
interventions to promote the benefits of physical activity to older people. Regular
moderate exercise can help prevent disease, disability and to some extent isolation,
among older people.

Thank you for your help in this important study.

Yours sincerely

A. Diamond

Alana Diamond
Research Project Manager

Approach letters

HAMILTON HOUSE · MABLEDON PLACE · LONDON WC1H 9TX · TEL 0171 383 3833 · FAX 0171 387 0550

P5620 / G

A research study for the Health Education Authority on exercise and physical activity :

Thank you for agreeing to take part in this research which is about how people regard exercise and physical activity. The study is being carried out by Social & Community Planning Research, an independent research institute. The aim is to explore how people feel about doing exercise, whether it's brisk walking, swimming, playing a sport, or any physical activity - to talk about what holds people back from being more active. Whether or not you do any exercise, we are interested in your views.

We are getting together small groups of about seven or eight people, in different parts of the country. The group discussion you have kindly agreed to attend will take place on:

Date: ....

Time: ....

Place: ....

The discussion should last about 1-1½ hours. Everything that you say will be treated as confidential: you will not be identified by name in any report on the research. We will be giving participants £15 as a small token of thanks for your help.

Yours sincerely

A. Diamond

Alana Diamond
Researcher

If you have any queries please contact Helen Finch on 0171 250 1866

HAMILTON HOUSE · MABLEDON PLACE · LONDON WC1H 9TX · TEL 0171 383 3833 · FAX 0171 387 0550

P5620 / D
October 1996

A research study for the Health Education Authority
on exercise and physical activity

Thank you for agreeing to take part in this research which is about how people regard exercise and physical activity. The study is being carried out by Social & Community Planning Research, an independent research institute. The aim is to explore how people feel about doing exercise, whether it's walking, dancing, swimming, or any physical activity - to talk about what holds people back from being more active or what attracts us to do it.

Whether or not you do any exercise, we are interested in your views. Research has already been conducted among young people. This study focuses on older age groups.

As agreed, the interviewer will call on: ....

at: ....

The interview will last about an hour. Everything that you say will be treated as confidential: you will not be identified by name in any report on the research. We will be giving participants £15 as a token of thanks for your help.

Yours sincerely

A. Diamond

Alana Diamond
Researcher
If you have any queries please contact Helen Finch on 0171 250 1866

Topic guide

Head Office: 35 NORTHAMPTON SQUARE,
LONDON EC1V 0AX
Tel: 0171-250 1866 Fax: 0171-250 1524

Field and DP Office: 100 KINGS ROAD,
BRENTWOOD, ESSEX CM14 4LX
Tel: 01277 200600 Fax: 01277 214117

P5620   **Exercise and physical activity**   October 1996

Topic guide

Key issues:

* What is known about physical activity and its benefits
* Attitudes to physical activity and participation
* Main barriers and main motivators
* Ways of overcoming barriers

INTRODUCTION

1. Background

* Household composition
* Employment activity (Working/ retired/ voluntary work/ looking after family, etc.)
* Hobbies
* How generally get about (to shops/friends/etc.)? E.g. car, bicycle, walk

COLLECT ALL ABOVE INFORMATION FROM EACH RESPONDENT

+ for DEPTHS and INSTITUTIONS: Age
                                       Length of time lived here
                                       What job/work used to do

2. What do we mean by 'physical activity'?
[brief section]

* What counts as 'physical activity'?...
  PROMPT IF NECESSARY:
  E.g. Does Walking count?/ Gardening?/ Housework?/ Dancing?/
        The kind of paid/voluntary work they do?

* Exercise or physical activity they do nowadays, if any? *(briefly)*
  - What activity(s)?
          - How often?
          - How long for?
          - What intensity?
  - Part of routine? Scheduled into the day/week?
  - Who with? Done alone? / With someone else? - Who?

1

BELIEFS

3. Beliefs / knowledge about physical activity and its benefits
[Key section]

- Is physical activity <u>important</u>?

  In what way? (Why bother? Why do it? What's the point?)
  DO NOT PROMPT INITIALLY, BUT PROBE: - Is it important for:
    - fitness?
    - health?   [Is 'fitness' different from 'health'?...
                     What understood by 'fitness'?]
        - heart/ stroke/ blood pressure/ diabetes/ osteoporosis / etc
        - any other health aspects?
    - weight control?
    - mental health?
    - general well being?
    - physical independence in old age?
    - reducing risk of injury/accident,
         e.g. falling and breaking a leg
    - other reasons?

- Does it matter:
    - <u>what sort</u> of physical activity they do (for health/fitness)?
    - <u>how much</u> physical exercise they do to keep fit/healthy? (how long for)
    - <u>how intensely</u> they do it?... Does it matter .. if get out of breath?
                                 .... or feel heart beat?

  DO NOT PROBE INITIALLY
  (Any mention or distinction made between - suppleness
                                          - strength
                                          - flexibility?)

- Physical activity as they get older
  - changing importance? e.g. dangers?

IN ALL THIS, DISTINGUISH:

** **General vs personal** importance of physical activity:
        Is it important generally? - e.g. thought to be a link
        Is it important on a personal level? - to them individually in everyday life

** Differences in importance as get older, and for their **particular age group**?
        More or less important? And in what way?
        [E.g. 'It's for younger people' / 'Want to rest now, put feet up' / etc.]

** **Sources** of any beliefs expressed

2

- Where does physical activity rate in comparison with other things they [might] do for their **health**? (+ Why position here?)
  PROBE: Is it more or less important than: - not smoking?
                                               - not drinking?
                                               - diet?
                                               - sleep?
                                               - stress, not worrying?

- How does it rate in relation to other activities **in general** that they do?
  i.e. Priority given to physical activity in their own lives (in practice)?

- The ideal : How would they <u>like</u> to prioritise it?
  - Like to do more?   What like to do?
  Aims in terms of fitness, now, as older, and in relation to the type of life they lead.
  (Have these goals changed over the years? What are they now?
        e.g. simply the ability to get up out of chair?)

4.   Activity levels now vs past

- How does physical activity that they do now compare with what they used to do, in the past?...   Changes over life? Why?
  PROBE: - type   )
            - level   ) → of physical activity done in past
            - duration   )   (<u>any</u> physical activity: sport/exercise/other)

3

BARRIERS

5. Perceived barriers to physical activity
[Key section]

- What prevents them from being more physically active?
  DO NOT PROMPT INITIALLY

PROBE FULLY :

- PAST EXPERIENCES - Have any past experiences put them off?

- FEAR - related to beliefs, eg 'dangerous to do too much'
  - practical / environmental, eg safety when going out

- MEDIA, e.g. newspaper accounts: *'Heart attack on squash court'* variety

- TIMES OF LIFE - Are there times in life when physical activity is
  more difficult? / or less important?
NB BARRIERS RELATED TO PHYSICAL ACTIVITY IN OLDER AGE
  - *PROBE FULLY* - Are there different barriers?
  E.g. Confidence...
  Perceived inability...
  Embarrassment...
  Other...

- COST
Is lack of money a barrier to physical activity?
(eg entrance/joining fees?? Awareness of o.a.p. discounts??)
Cost compared to other things? E.g. going out/ hiring a video film

- LACK OF MOTIVATION - lack of incentive??
  E.g. 'Just for young people' / 'Can't be bothered' (Why?)
  Loss of someone to do it with?
What would make a difference?

- TIME
Is lack of time a barrier to physical activity when retired?
How spend time generally? What sort of routine?
Why/ how is lack of time a barrier?
  eg busy caring for others (grandchildren or other elderly people)?
What like to do with their time?

- OTHER BARRIERS??

4

MOTIVATORS

6. Overcoming the barriers

- How could these barriers be overcome?...

Key motivators are known to be:	1. Fun
[-research among older people in Germany]	2. Sociability
	3. Health

  PROBE WHAT THIS MEANS FOR THEM

  What [would] <u>like</u> about doing physical activity. Reasons to do it
  e.g. Get fit for a particular reason - keep up with grandchild, etc

- How do people who are more active overcome barriers?...
  What motivators?   Appearance, weight? Etc...
  IF ACTIVE IN PAST: How come then, at different times?

- Would active promotion help? *[LEAD-IN TO NEXT SECTION]*

7. Promotional strategies / ideas

- <u>Know</u> of any information or promotional material on physical activity?
  [HEA 'Active For Life' campaign, including TV ad, launched April '96]
  - Heard or seen anything at all [from any source]? (What? Where?)
  - What did they think of it? How did they respond? Had an effect?

- <u>Want</u> to be told? (Or is it nannying, or patronising?)
  Extent want to be told? Prescription or just encouragement, basic ideas?

- Is there a <u>need</u> for more information / advice?
  E.g. Literature or promotions (What kind? / Why?)

- <u>Who</u> (where) would look to for guidance re information on benefits
  of physical activity?

- How would they promote it (if they were the HEA) to people in
  their age group?   - What would be the best way?
                            - What would work for them?

- Response to HEA **general** message: *'Warm and slightly out of breath'*,
          cf for **older** people: *'Warm and breathe more heavily than usual'*.

- How respond to these?

- Other ideas?

                    - THE END -

5